OFFICIAL

CB

DICTIONARY

LATEST TERMS & DEFINITIONS
OF CITIZENS BAND JARGON

THE NEW LANGUAGE OF
MILLIONS OF PEOPLE ON THE GO

Including
OVER 1000 DEFINITIONS
CB 10 CODE
FCC RULES
Required by Law to be kept with CB Set

BOOK CRAFT-GUILD, INC.
NEW YORK, N.Y.

OFFICIAL
CB DICTIONARY

TABLE OF CONTENTS

Foreword   7

CB Language Dictionary
CB To English   15

Cross Reference
English To CB   61

Ten Codes Introduction
Complete Ten Code   77
Abbreviated or CB 10 Code   80
Law Enforcement Ten Code   81
International Phonetic Alphabet   84

Inexpensive "Bear Buster"
CB Converter for AM Car Radio   85

Q-Signals   86

Current and Official CB Radio
Rules and Regulations from the FCC   89

Transmitter Identification Card   123

The FCC Field Office Addresses   125

Directory of Manufacturers   128

FCC Form 505   130

Notes   132

CB Radio Log   133

Foreword

Civilian Band (CB) radio has been called "the biggest explosion in communications since the invention of the telephone." It is active, not passive like television viewing. CBers feel that they are taking part in a huge radio "talk show," or on a sort of telephone "party line" that reaches along the ten to fifteen-mile range of their sets.

Nearly all CB sets are "transceivers." That is, they both transmit and receive radio messages. In itself, CB radio is not new. It is closely related to other kinds of radio such as police and ship-to-shore, and frequencies have been allocated to its specific use by the Federal Communications Commission (FCC) since 1947.

For many years, CBers—farmers and hunters and boatsmen and lonely over-the-road truckers, mostly—operated on the "eleven meter band" of radio frequency without anybody paying much attention to them. Then several things happened that put CB radio suddenly and explosively in the forefront of modern communications.

One was the oil embargo in 1973 that made fuel, particularly diesel fuel for truckers, hard to find. Efficient communications were vital if these truckers were not to be stranded in strange towns.

Another was the national fifty-five miles per hour speed limit. This again created a crisis for truckers, because time to them is money and too many hours on the road could mean the difference between profit and loss. But speeding tickets were expensive and time-consuming, too, so truckers needed to know the whereabouts of highway police.

Thus CB mushroomed into popularity as a means of communication among truckers about sources of fuel, locations of speed traps, and information on local road conditions. The general public was not slow to recognize the usefulness of CB.

So warm has been public acceptance of the new medium that sales of CB sets, and issuance by the U.S. Government of compulsory licenses to operate them, have grown literally by the millions in each of recent years. Almost as many CB sets are sold as television sets. It is estimated at this writing that more than half of all trucks now are CB-equipped, and passenger cars are climbing rapidly toward that figure. In fact, CB radios are now optional equipment on most new cars.

Because licenses are compulsory, there was a glut of paperwork for a time at the government agency that issues them. This is the FCC office in Gettysburg, Pa., which has solved the problem by issuing temporary licenses which are valid until it can issue permanent ones.

Enthusiasts predict that CB radios are so useful that they will be compulsory equipment on all cars one day. Is this over-optimism? Is CB just a passing fad?

Hardly, most experts agree. There have been problems associated with its explosive growth, but these problems have been or are being solved. CB has too many uses, and has come to occupy too important a place in many people's lives, for it to be cast aside lightly.

Long-distance truckers have been, and will probably continue to be, the backbone of the CB movement. In addition to providing valuable highway information, CB combats boredom and keeps drivers alert. Truck drivers' use of amphetamines has declined drastically with CB's rising popularity. But these aristocrats of the highways are far from being the only ones who now find CB indispensible. Many traveling salesmen, for example, say that they'd rather leave behind their spare tire than their CB set.

Vacationers, too, find many uses for CB in addition to highway information. They can call ahead for reservations (many motels monitor CB), check fishing or skiing or weather conditions at their destination, ask local residents about restaurants, call for help if they're lost or stranded. They can even call a taxi if they're in a motor home and would rather not unpack it, because many cab companies, especially in smaller towns, are CB-equipped. And many garages along well-traveled routes also monitor CB and will send help in case of breakdown.

Then too, listening to local "ratchet jawing" can add to the traveler's knowledge of the territory he's passing through. He can even talk to farmers out in the fields on their tractors and combines because many of these are CB-equipped. All in all, CB is proving to be a great boon to this "nation on wheels."

It has uses closer to home, too. If he has his "ears on," a CBer can learn of rush-hour traffic jams and take an alternate route home. For an additional outlay he can install a "base station" in his home or office and thereby expand his set's usefulness greatly. With this station he can call his office for messages, or his home that he'll be late for dinner. And his wife can call to ask him to bring home an extra loaf of bread.

The kids can be equipped with "walkie talkies" so they can report to Mom at the "base station" every half hour or so when they're outside playing. These small, portable sets can also be used in conjunction with CB in the family car when on vacation.

Shut-ins and those living in remote areas often find CB to be of even greater use, and adding even more to their sense of security than the telephone. And one of the most useful of all applications of CB has been to emergency and rescue work. There are several volunteer organizations who monitor CB emergency radio channels. One of them, REACT (Radio Emergency Associated Citizens Teams) claims to have handled 35 million emergency calls, including 12 million highway accidents, since its formation in 1962.

It is undeniable that CB is more than amply demonstrating its usefulness and that its future as a communications medium is assured. And nothing succeeds like success. The more CBers there are, the more people want to become CBers.

All the foregoing are reasons for CB's surging popularity. But probably the single most important reason is the almost unlimited opportunity that CB gives one to talk to other people. "Modulating" with "good buddies" promotes a feeling of neighborliness that is rare for most of us in today's increasingly impersonal society, and an unprecedented antidote to the anonymity and isolation that most of us feel when we're encapsulated in our cars on the highway.

With CB, you can ask for information without shyness, and you'll be amazed how readily other CBers give their help. Very shortly, you'll find that you are being helpful in return. It's a way to form personal relationships—most of them of very short duration—without becoming deeply involved. There are no permanent ties, as there would be in joining a church or political group, for example, but the personal satisfaction in the way of friendly communication is in some ways the same.

Federal regulations require that you give your "call sign"—the numbers and letters on your FCC license—whenever you transmit. You may also use your "handle"—your own pet nickname for yourself. Most CBers use only the "handle" and skip the "call sign"—a breach of regulations so common that it probably couldn't be punished even if the FCC were so minded.

These "handles" tell a lot about the way a person views himself. A sedate businessman named Gordon calls himself "Flash;" a matron perhaps wistfully calls herself "Kissy Face." Both may be acting out private fantasies. But "Bra Buster" is not acting out anything. She's all business, one of the more notorious "pavement princesses" (see CB-English Dictionary in this volume).

If you want to pretend on CB, you can go ahead and do it. Except for your "handle," you're anonymous. You can let other CBers think, for example, that you're in an expensive Porsche instead of the rattletrap Chevie they just passed in the "struggle lane" on the last long upgrade. In this respect, CB is somewhat like a singles bar. If it gives you satisfaction, you can pretend to be anything you want, and you'll probably get away with it.

CB, then, can be an expression of fantasy. It can make every man equal. There are no rich men and poor men among CBers, only strong signals and weak ones. And as long as there's CB, there is little fear that America will become a police state. Much of CB's appeal is an expression of the distaste that most of us have for Authority.

There are more synomyms for "police" and "police car" and "radar" and all the other authoritarian accoutrements than for any other words in this Dictionary. A few are insulting; most are whimsical or just good, clean fun.

CBers think of themselves, as a group, as the "good guys" and the "Smokies" as the "bad guys." This is the theme of a form of sub-culture that is growing around CB radio. There have been hit tunes, movies, even a comic strip character, "Snoopy," who has become a CB nut, and even a porno movie called "CB Mamas." This last shows that the makers of the porno film didn't know what they were talking about because a "mama" is a kind of CB antenna (see Dictionary).

The air waves are for the use of everyone. With so many people using them, government regulation is desirable and necessary. But there have been attempts at over-regulation with the FCC viewing itself as a sort of "Big Brother." An example is the idea of having "identifiers" built into CB sets at the factory. These would automatically identify each sender every time he used his microphone. By consulting a master list, the FCC could then find out who was saying what. The American Civil Liberties Union (ACLU) threatened to sue the FCC for violation of civil rights; the FCC abandoned the idea; CB radio still represents the expression in this country of human rights and liberties.

Other countries are not so liberal. Regulations are stricter in some of them, and a few Western democracies ban CB radio entirely. We have no word of CB behind the Iron Curtain, and most conclude that it does not exist.

Every "in" group, no matter where, has its own private jargon so that its members may recognize each other and communicate without outsiders understanding. Lawyers speak of torts and doctors write their prescriptions in Latin. Just like other groups, CB has its own private language, too. Within a few short years it has outdated every slang dictionary ever written.

CB is often a funny language. It is even poetic sometimes without being in any way highbrow, because it has some imaginative figures of speech. It's not a hard language to learn. In fact, it's easy. But you need a dictionary like this to help you overcome "mike fright" and get started. Even if you're a CB veteran, you'll find words and phrases here that you never knew before.

Even after you've mastered the vocabulary, though, you'll have trouble convincing people that you're a "big rigger." These jockeys of the "eighteen wheelers" are the acknowledged kings of the road. For some reason, most of them seem to speak with a Texarklahoma accent. Whether it's native or not, the accent sounds convincing. But this accent takes a little practice, and you'll have to work up to it.

Meanwhile, you are clean and green. Put the pedal to the metal and keep the shiny side up and the greasy side down. Ten fur? Stack them eights, good buddy. Down and gone.

CB

Language Directory

Like all living language, CB is in a state of constant change. This is the latest version of it: rich, often funny, drawn from many sources. Nearly all of it will be understood wherever you go. However, a few words are in regional use, and are so marked: (M) for Midwest, (W) for West, and so on. Read this CB Language Dictionary for fun, and keep it near your CB rig for handy reference.

A

Abuse it: Masturbate. (Usually used in friendly banter between truckers.)

Adios: Singing off; goodbye (W).

Advertising: Markings on police car.

AF: Audio Frequency; range of 15 to 20,000 cycles per second which is normally audible sound.

Affirmative: Yes.

Afterburner: See "Linear Amplifier."

ALERT: Affiliated League of Emergency Radio Teams.

Alligator: Talkative CBer; all mouth and no ears.

All right: Safe; closed; gone.

Example: "Smokey's all right" means police have left.

AM: Amplitude Modulation; most standard car radios and CB sets operate on this kind of radio signal.

Amplifier: Component of CB set which increases power.

Anchored Modulator: Home or fixed base CB set.

Anchor it: Stop.

ANL: Automatic Noise Limiter to reduce atmospheric static and most engine radio "noise."

Apple: Illegal CB set operator.

Around the Horn: Tune through all 23 CB channels.

Aviator: Speeding driver.

B

Baby bear: Rookie policeman.

Back: Over to you.

Back door: Last vehicle in a CB convoy.

Back door closed: Police car tailing last vehicle in a CB convoy.

Back down (or up): Slow to legal speed limit; slow down or stop transmitting.

Background: Noise interfering with CB reception.

Back Off: Slow down.

Back out: Stop transmitting.

Backside: Return trip.

Backstroke: Return trip.

Back yard: The road behind.

Bag: Catch, apprehend.

Ballmer: Baltimore, Md.

Bang: Make or hang. Example: "Bang a left at that big slab."

Bar City: Many towns qualify—perhaps your own.

Barefoot: Legal, unmodified CB power.

Barn: Truck garage.

Basement: Channel 1 on CB set.

Base station: CB set at fixed location; also "Anchored Modulator."

Bay City: San Francisco.

Be: Am; are; deliberately ungrammatical use affected by many CBers. For example: "Bears be in them bushes."

Beam: Highly directional type antenna.

Bean Town: Boston, Mass.

Bear: Police.

Bear bait: Speeding motorist without CB.

Bear bite: Speeding ticket.

Bear buster: CB converter installed on regular AM car radio to permit monitoring CB broadcasts without transmitting.

Bear cage (or cave or den): Police station.

Bear food: Same as bear bait.

Bear in the air (or sky): Police helicopter.

Bear in the bushes: Speed trap.

Bear meat: Same as bear bait.

Bear on skates: Police in moving vehicle.

Bear report (or story): Information on police whereabouts.

Bear trap: Speed trap.

Bearded buddy: Policeman.

Bears crawling: Police on both sides of highway.

Bears wall to wall: Police all over the place.

Beat the bushes: Lead vehicle or "front door" of CB convoy; will warn others of police or road hazards. Also, speeding slightly to attract police attention but not enough to receive ticket.

Beaver: Woman.

Beaver hunt (or patrol): Looking for female companionship.

Beaver meter: "S" meter on CB radio.

Beaver, three-legged: Male homosexual.

Bedbug hauler: Moving van.

Bedroom, movable: Camper; motor home; small van equipped for sleeping.

Beer can: Beer delivery truck.

Beer City: Milwaukee, Wis.

Belly up: Overturned car.

Bending windows: Clear CB transmission.

Bennie-chaser: Coffee

Bennies: Benzedrine pills, to avoid falling asleep.

Better half: Spouse; girl friend.

Between sheets: Bed; sleeping.

Bible: "Golden Rule" safe-driving book. Also, log book.

Big A: Atlanta, Ga.; Amarillo, Tex.

Big Apple: New York City.

Big Car: Eighteen-wheeler, tractor-trailer, semi.

Big D : Dallas, Tex.

Big Dog: Greyhound bus.

Big ears: Clear reception of CB signal.

Big hat: State trooper.

Big M: Memphis, Tenn.

Big mama: Tall radio antenna.

Big Orange: Snyder truck.

Big R: Roadway Freight System truck.

Big rig: Truck, semi, tractor-trailer.

Big rigger: Cocky or proud driver.

Big slab: Turnpike or expressway.

Big switch: On-off switch of CB radio set.

Big T: Tucson, Ariz.

Big ten-four: Enthusiastic agreement or thanks. (Also big four-ten.)

Bikini state: Florida.

Binders: Brakes.

Bird: Ford Thunderbird; police helicopter.

Birdyback: Hauling freight to or from an air cargo terminal.

Bit of the seat of the britches: Got a ticket.

Black and white: Police car.

Black water: Coffee.

Bleeding: Interference caused by talk on nearby channels.

Blind side: The right side.

Blinkin' winkin': School bus.

Blinky: Vehicle with one headlight out.

Blocking the channel: CB interference; holding microphone button down.

Blood box: Ambulance.

Blow the doors off (or in): Passing another vehicle quickly.

Blower: Supercharger.

Blowing smoke: Clear transmission.

Blown pumpkin (or doughnut): Flat tire.

Blue and white: Police (some states).

Blue Grass State: Kentucky.

Blue jeans: State police.

Blue light: Police car.

Blue slip: Speeding ticket.

Bob tail: Truck without trailer. Also, non-CB equipped vehicle following one equipped with CB.

Bodacious: Loud and clear signal; anything that is very good.

Bodayshush: Same as "Bodacious."

Bogey: Two or more vehicle axles in tandem.

Bone box: Hearse or ambulance.

Boob tube: Television.

Boogieing: Nightclubbing.

Boogie man: State trooper; Smokey the Bear.

Boom it down: Tighten the load.

Boom wagon: Truck carrying dangerous cargo.

Boomer: Tie-down device to tighten chain on flat-bed trailer.

Boondocking: Driving back roads to avoid weight stations.

Bootleg: Illegal CB set or operator.

Bottle popper: Beverage truck.

Bra buster: Large-busted woman. (Originally was "handle" of a specific "Pavement princess.")

Break: Interruption; what to say when one wants permission to transmit. For example: "Break one niner" means that one wishes to transmit on Channel 19. Also, "Break, break."

Break, broke: Same as "Break, break."

Break the unit: Uncouple tractor and trailer.

Breaker: Same as "Break." Also refers to the person saying, "Break." Also, "Breaker, breaker."

Breaking the needle: Clear reception of signal.

Breaking up: Poor reception; signal fading or not constant.

Breaking wind: First CB-equipped vehicle in a convoy; the "front door."

Breeze it: Forget it.

Brew: Beer.

Bring it back: Repeat transmission; answer question.

Bring it on: Please reply. Also, come on up here; the way is clear.

Bring it on in: Please reply. Also, move to your right.

Bring it on up: Everything is okay; no police.

Brown bottle: Beer.

Brown paper bag: Unmarked police car.

Brush your teeth and comb your hair: Police radar ahead.

B-Town: Birmingham, Ala.

Bubble gum machine: Police car equipped with flashing light.

Bubblegummer: Teenager.

Bubble trouble: Tire trouble.

Bucket mouth: Gossiper; loud, profane or obscene talker.

Bucket of bolts: Truck, tractor, trailer, rig.

Buckeye State: Ohio.

Buddy: Fellow CBer, especially when "handle" not known. Often, "Good buddy."

Buffalo: Man, guy, husband.

Bulldog: Mack truck.

Bullet lane: Passing lane.

Bull hauler: Excessive or idle talker. Also livestock trucker.

Bull jockey: Same as "Bull hauler."

Bull rack: Cattle truck, bulls, police.

Bumper jumper: Tail gater.

Bumper lane: Passing lane.

Bushel: Half-ton. A 10-ton load is 20 bushels.

Button-pusher: One who keys his microphone without talking. This causes electronic noise and interferes with messages.

Buy the farm: Get killed.

Buy the orchard: Become involved in an accident or misfortune.

By: Standing by.

Bye-bye: Signing off.

C

Cab: Part of truck driver sits in.

Cackle crate: Truck hauling live poultry.

Cactus juice: Liquor (W).

California turnarounds: Sleep-avoiding pills; "bennies."

Call sign: Official FCC assignment of letters and numbers to a radio operator; calling, asking for, paging.

Camel back: Truck body sloping to the rear.

Camera: Police radar.

Candy man: FCC inspector.

Casa: Home (W).

Catch car: Police car working in conjunction with radar to stop speeders.

Catch you: Talk to you again.

CB: Citizens Band radio transmitter-receiver.

Cement mixer: Truck with nosy engine or gears.

Channel: Any of 23 CB frequencies from 26.965 to 27.255 MHz.

Channel nine: For emergency use only.

Channel nineteen: For CBers on the road.

Channel ten: Used by some truckers.

Charlie (or Uncle Charlie): FCC.

Chase car: Same as catch car.

Chew 'n' choke: Restaurant.

Chicken choker: Poultry truck. Also masturbater; friendly term among truckers.

Chicken coop: Truck weighing station.

Chicken inspector: Man in charge of truck weighing station.

Chief hood lifter: Garage superintendent.

Chi; Chi Town: Chicago, Ill.

Choke 'n' puke: Restaurant.

Choking the Chicken: Masturbation.

Choo-choo Town: Chattanooga, Tenn.

Chopper: Helicopter.

Christmas card: Speeding ticket.

Chucking carriers: Keying the microphone deliberately to keep others from talking.

Cigar City: Tampa, F a.

Circle City: Tampa, Fla.

Circle City: Indianapolis, Ind.

Circus wagon: Low-sided trailer with high tarpaulin cover.

City flyer: Short, low trailer for local deliveries.

City Kitty: Local police.

Class A: Radio transmitter authorized by FCC to operate in 460-470 MHz UHF band with power of no more than 50 watts.

Class B: Operations terminated.

Class C: Radio transmitter authorized for specific frequency in 26.96 to 27.26 or 72 to 76 MHz band for control of remote objects.

Class D: CB station for radio telephony in 26.96 to 27.26 MHz band.

Clean: No police, accidents or obstructions.

Clean shot: All clean and green ahead.

Clean side: New Jersey (E).

Clean up: Be sexually promiscuous.

Clear: Transmission completed; finished talking.

Clear after you: There will be no one on this channel after you sign off.

Clear and rolling: I am finished transmitting and starting to drive.

Close the gate: Shut rear doors.

Coal: Power. Example: "Shovel on the coal."

Co-ax: Coaxial cable.

Cockleburr: Pep pill (W).

Coffee break: Informal gathering; also visit with a prostitute.

Coffee pot: Restaurant.

Coffin or coffin box: Sleeper compartment behind truck cab.

Coke stop: Restroom break.

Cold Coffee: Beer.

Cold rig: Tractor pulling refrigerated trailer.

Collect call: Message for a specific CBer.

Colorado Kool Aid: Coors beer.

Colors up: Lights on police car turned on.

Come again: Repeat last transmission.

Come-along: Cummins Diesel type of power plant for a tractor.

Come back: Same as "Come again."

Come here: Same as "Come again."

Come on: Your turn to talk; "Over."

Comic book: Trucker's log.

Coming in: Signal is being received.

Common gas: Regular gasoline.

Compadre: Brother or good buddy.

Concentrator: Driver.

Concrete jungle: Expressway.

Converter: Device to receive but not transmit CB conversations. (See "Bear Buster.")

Convoy: Group of vehicles traveling same road in same direction and in CB contact with each other.

Cook shack: Truck stop.

Cookies: Cigarettes.

Cool it: Slow down.

Cop shop: Police station.

Copy: Hear and understand message.

Copy cat: Anyone repeating reports given by another operator. Operator on air waves saying nothing of importance.

Copy the mail: Listen at home, not on the road.

Corn Binder: International Harvester truck.

Corn cellar: Liquor store.

Cotton Mouth: Thirsty.

Cotton picker: Anybody, usually friendly term. However, can be used as substitute for obscenity.

Country Cadillac: Sporty pickup truck such as Chevrolet El Camino or Ford Ranchero.

County Mountie: County police.

Cover: Girl.

Covered up: Signal is muffled.

Cowboy: Reckless driver.

Cowboy truck: Truck with lots of chrome.

Cow town: Fort Worth, Tex.

Crank up the mike: Turn up the preamplifier.

Creeper gear: Compound low gear for maximum pulling power.

CRS: Citizens Radio Service; part of FCC which regulates CB radio.

Cruising around: Leisurely driving.

CRW: Community Radio Watch. CB service comprised of volunteers who monitor emergency Channel 9.

Cuda: Plymouth Barracuda

Cut loose: Stop transmitting; sign off.

Cut the co-ax: Sign off. Turn off the CB set.

Cut (or log) some Get some sleep.

D

Dago: San Diego, Calif.

DDT: Warning; Don't Do That.

Dead heading: Running empty.

Dead pedal: Slow-moving vehicle.

Decibel: (dB) unit of sound measurement.

Decoy: Unmanned police car.

Definitely: Strong affirmative.

Delta tune: Control to fine-tune frequency on some CB sets slightly off-center and compensate for frequency variations in other CB transmitters.

Derby City: Louisville, Ky.

Detroit vibrator: Chevrolet truck.

Diarrhea mouth: Excessive talker.

Dice City: Las Vegas, Nev.

Diesel car: Diesel digit.

Dirty City: New York City; Cleveland; Pittsburgh.

Dirty floor: Unpaved parking lot.

Dirty side: East Coast, especially New York and Pennsylvania.

Ditch light: Spotlight aimed at right side of road.

Dock walloper: One who loads and unloads freight.

Dog: Greyhound bus.

Dog house: Cover over engine.

Dog, walking the: Operating CB set.

Do it to me: Please answer.

Do you copy: Do you understand?

Doin' it to it: Going full speed.

Doin' it to it, that way: Sign off.

Donkey: Tail; rear; "back door." Example ; "I'll watch the front door and you watch the donkey."

DOT: Canadian Department of Transport, equivalent to FCC in USA.

Dot man: Department of Transportation representative who checks trucks' conformity to regulations. Also indicates weighing station.

Double bottom: Twin trailers.

Double buffalo: 55 miles per hour.

Double eighty-eights: Love and kisses.

Double L: Land line, telephone.

Double nickel: 55 miles per hour.

Doubles: Twin trailers.

Double seven: Negative.

Douche job: Wash.

Doughnut: Tire.

Down: Sign off.

Down and gone: Signed off and stopped listening.

Down and on the side: Finished transmitting, but still listening.

Downed: Stuck.

Down in the corner: Lowest gear (see "Creeper.")

Drag down: Shift gears slowly.

Draggin' wagon: Tow truck, wrecker.

Dress for sale: Prostitute.

Driving the peg: Driving the legal limit.

Drop off the shoulder: Run off the road.

Drop the body: Uncouple trailer; see "break rig."

Drop the carrier: Key the microphone, preventing transmission.

Drop the hammer: Accelerate.

Dry carriers: Keying microphone deliberately to block channel; see "chucking carriers."

Dudley Do Right: Missouri State highway patrolman.

Dummy: Unmanned police car.

Dust britches: Pass.

Dust ears: Interrupt transmission.

Dusting: Driving on shoulder or road.

DX: Long Distance.

E

Ears: CB set.

Easy Chair: In the middle between "front door" and "back door" of a CB convoy, and thus able to relax a little; also "rocking chair."

Eat-'em-up stop: Truckers' restaurant.

EIA: Electronics Industries Association.

Eight and other good numbers: Sign off; best wishes.

Eighteen-legged pogo stick: 18 wheel tractor-trailer.

Eighteen-wheeler: Big tractor-trailer; also applicable to 14 and 22-wheelers.

Eights: Sign-off.

Eighty-eights: Love and kisses.

Electric teeth: Police.

Eleven-meter band: 27 MHz citizens band, formerly 11-meter amateur radio band.

ERP: Effective radiated power; may be more or less than transmitter power depending on antenna system.

ERS: Emergency Radio Service: CB Channel 9.

Expressway boogie: Long highway haul.

Extra money: Speeding ticket.

Eyeball: Have in sight; also informal meeting.

Eye in the sky: Police helicopter.

Evel Knievel: Motorcycle rider.

Evel Knievel Smokey: Motorcycle rider.

Evel Knievel Smokey: Police motorcycle rider; also fast-moving police car.

F

Fat load: Overweight cargo.

FCC: Federal Communications Commission; regulatory body for CB radio.

Fed: DOT or FCC inspector.

Feed the horses (or ponies): Lose betting on horse races.

Fifth Wheel: Load-bearing coupling between tractor and trailer.

Fifty-dollar lane: Passing lane on a highway.

Final: Last transmission; out.

Finger wave: Obscene gesture.

Fireworks: Many police cars with lights on.

First sergeant: Wife.

Fish: Plymouth Barracuda.

Fishing pole and a partner: Two antennas.

Fishyback: Transporting truck trailers by ship.

Five by five: Strong signal received.

Five-finger discount: Stolen.

Five-Five: 55 miles per hour.

Fix: Report on police location.

Fix-Or-Repair Daily: Ford truck.

Fixed station: Immobile radio transmitter.

Flagwaver: Lead construction worker.

Flake: Used instead of four-letter word.

Flakey: Same as "Flake."

Flashlight Shirt: Man's shirt with mother-of-pearl snaps or buttons.

Flick: Movie.

Flight man: Motorized weigh station worker (S, W).

Flip: Return trip. Also "flipper"; "flipside."

Flip-flop: Return trip; also, change direction.

Floater: Truck driver without steady job.

Floating the gears: Clutchless gear shifting.

Floats: Large single tires.

Flop it: Turn around.

Fluff stuff: Snow.

Flyboy: Speeder.

Fly in the Sky: Police aircraft.

Folding cameras: Portable speed monitors in some police cars.

Foot in the carburetor (or firewall or radiator): Throttle wide open.

Foot warner: Homemade or illegal linear amplifier.

For sure: Affirmative, correct.

Forty-footer: Big tractor-trailer; same as 18-wheeler.

Forty-fours: Children; kisses.

Forty-over: Loud and clear.

Forty-roger: 10-4; okay; message acknowledged.

Forty weight: Beer (SW)

Four: Same as 10-4; 40-roger.

Four banger: Four-speed gearbox.

Four-by-four: Blazer, Bronco or Jeep; small four-wheel drive vehicle.

Four D: Same as 10-4.

Four-lane parking lot: Four-legged beast.

Four-legged go-go dancers: Cargo of live animals, especially pigs.

Four-roger: Definite, affirmative.

Four-wheeler: Passenger car, light van or small truck.

Four wheeler with fire in his tail: Speeding car without CB.

Fox hunting: FCC monitoring CBers for profanity or other illegal use of equipment.

Free ride: Prostitute, often an amateur.

Frequency synthesizer: Circuit for transmission and reception on several channels without separate crystals.

Frilly blouse: Pretty woman.

Frisco: San Francisco.

Front door: Road ahead; lead vehicle responsible for warning other vehicles in CB convoy and also CB-equipped vehicles going in other direction.

Front end: Lead vehicle in CB convoy.

Fruitliner: White Motor Co. truck.

Fun City: New York City.

Funny books: Pornography.

Funny bunny: Disguised police car.

Fuzz buster: Device for detecting radar.

G

Gain: Volume control on a CB set.

Gambling Town: Las Vegas, Nev.

Gandy Dancer: Road construction worker.

Gateway City: St. Louis, Mo.

GBY: God Bless You.

Gear: Speed in truck transmission. Also, equipment as in "CB" gear."

Gear banger: Trucker. Also, driver who · clashes gears when shifting.

Gear jammer: Same as gear banger.

Georgia overdrive: Neutral gear in transmission, used illegally for coasting. Also, "Mexican overdrive" or "Midnight overdrive."

Get horizontal: Go to bed.

Girlie bear: Policewoman.

Give a shout: Answer.

Glad hands: Brake air lines between tractor and trailer. Also, trailer brakes.

Go ahead: Answer.

Goat 'n' shoat: Livestock.

Go back: Answer again; repeat.

Go, breaker: Go ahead. Grants permission for use of channel to one who has just requested it. See "Break," "Breaker."

Go down: Sign off; say goodbye.

Go-go girls: Pigs.

Going home hole: Top gear.

Go juice: Diesel fuel. Also, "Go-go juice."

Go 10-100: Make a restroom stop.

Golden Archway: St. Louis, Mo.

Goldilocks: Female CBer or driver.

Gone: Out; end transmission. Also, "Gone down."

Good buddy: Friendly term for fellow CBer, especially when "handle" is not known.

Goodied up: Fancily equipped.

Good numbers: Best wishes.

Good shot: Road ahead is clear.

Goonie bird: CB radio jammer.

Grab one: Shift into a lower gear.

Granny gear: Compound low gear. Same as "Creeper."

Grass: Median strip on highway. Also, marijuana.

Grasshopper: Park policeman.

Greasy side up: Overturned (vehicle).

Green apple: Inexperienced CBer.

Green CBer: Military police with CB.

Green light: Road clear; go ahead.

Green machine: US marines.

Greens: Money; speeding ticket.

Green stamp lane: Passing lane.

Green stamps: Speeding tickets; money.

Grizzly: Police.

Ground clouds: Fog.

Grounded: Driver outside vehicle. Example: "Lay an eyeball on that grounded smokey."

Growed-up trucks: Big tractor trailers; 18-wheelers.

Guarantoya: Strong affirmative; yes indeed.

Guitar Town: Nashville, Tenn.

Gump: Stolen chicken.

Gun runner: Police radar.

Gutter balling: Bowling.

Guy: Fellow trucker, usually CBer whose "Handle" is unknown.

H

Hag Bag: Prostitute; female tramp.

Ham: Amateur radio operator; not a CBer.

Hamburger helper: Linear amplifier.

Hammer: Gas pedal.

Hammer down: Accelerate. Also, "Hammer hanging," or "On."

Hammer off: Decelerate or stop. Also, "Hammer up."

Handle: Name, often whimsical, used by CBer for personal identification.

Hang: Make (a turn). Example: "Hang a right onto that big slab." Same as "Bang."

Hang it in your car: That's nonsense.

Hang it out: Monitor a CB channel.

Hangar: Home garage.

Hanging the needle: Strong signal; clear reception.

Happy numbers: Best wishes.

Hard ankle: Trucker; working man.

Harvey Wallbanger: Reckless driver.

Hash: Background noise; signal unclear. Also, "Hash and trash."

Hauling postholes: Empty.

Have a 36-24-36: Goodnight; signoff.

Hay-burning Smokey: Policeman mounted on horseback.

Heater: Linear amplifier.

Hemorrhoid with a Polaroid: Police car with radar.

Hidin' in the bushes: What bears do.

Hill Town: San Francisco, Calif.

Hillbilly music box: CB set.

Hillbilly opera: Country and western music.

Hillbilly wagon: GMC truck; any pickup truck.

Hind end: Last vehicle in a CB convoy; "Back door."

Hit: Reception; "How am I hitting you?"

Hole: Transmission gear or speed. Example: "I be in the goin' home hole."

Hole in the wall: Tunnel.

Holler: Call on CB radio.

Home port: Permanent residence.

Home twenty: Home location.

Honey bear: Policewoman.

Honey on the road: Warning; police everywhere. Example: "Honey on the road! Bears are swarming."

Honey wagon: Beer truck.

Hood lifter: Truck mechanic.

Hoo-hooer: Left lane hog.

Hopper body: Bottom-dumping truck body.

Hoppins: Stolen vegetables.

Horizontal: In bed.

Horse: Tractor trailer truck; Ford Mustang.

Horse light: Spotlight mounted on truck cab.

Horses: Horsepower.

Hot Lanta: Atlanta, Ga.

Hot load: Rush shipment.

Hot pants: Fire or smoke.

Hot stuff: Coffee.

Hot Town: Atlanta, Ga.

"How about that—one time?" Request for a specific CBer by name.

"How be we looking?": How's the road? (To trucker coming from opposite direction.)

How tall: What height.

Hump: Mountain.

Hundred-mile brew: Very strong coffee.

Hustler: CB antenna.

Hydroplane: Lose steering control on wet highway.

I

In a short short: Soon.

In the grass: On median strip.

Instamatic: Police radar.

Iron. Old truck.

J

Jack it around: Reverse to negotiate sharp turn.

Jack it up: Accelerate.

Jackrabbit: Policeman (W).

Jake: Truck brakes.

Jamboree: Large gathering of CBers.

Japanese toy: CB radio.

Jaw Jacking: CB conversation.

Jimmy: GMC truck.

Jockey: Truck or tractor-trailer driver; "professional."

John Law: Local police. Also, "Johnny."

Jump the pin: Accidental disconnection of fifth wheel between tractor and trailer.

Junk buzzard: Bum.

Junk yard: Home base; place of employment; garage.

K

Kenosha Cadillac: Any AMC car.

Key the mike: Activate microphone without transmitting voice signal.

Kick down: Shift to lower gear.

Kiddie car: School bus.

Kidney-buster: Hard-riding truck.

Knocked down: Unassembled freight or merchandise.

Knocking: Vehicle doing its best.

Knock it around: Drive at desired speed; road clear.

Knock the slack out: Accelerate.

Knuckle buster: Fist fight.

Kodak ; Police radar.

Kodiak: Policeman (W).

Kojak: Policeman.

Kool Aid: Liquor; beer; booze.

K-Whopper: Kenworth truck.

L

Lady breaker: Female CBer.

Land Line: Telephone. Also, "L.L."

Land of Disney: Disneyland (W).

Land of Wonderful: All clear ahead.

Landing gear: Support mechanism for front of trailer when not attached to tractor unit.

Latrine lips: Foul mouth.

Lay an eye on: See; look at.

Lay down: Stop transmitting.

Layin' and stayin': Doing one's best. Also, goodbye; sign-off.

Lay it over: Stand by.

Lay on the air: Apply brakes.

Left lane: Passing lane.

Left shoulder, over the: To the rear; in the opposite direction.

Legal beagle: Cber who adheres to correct CB procedures.

Legalized: Legal speed limit.

Let flaps down: Slow down.

Let it roll: Accelerate; get moving.

Let the channel roll: Let other people talk.

Let the hammer down: Accelerate; go fast.

Lettuce: Money.

Lid: Inept CB operator.

Lie sheet: Trucker' log book.

Light footing: Driving at legal speed limit.

Linear amplifier: Illegal CB power booster which increases power several hundred watts.

Lit candles: Police car's lights on. See "Bubble gum machine."

Little bears: Local police.

Little bit: Sexual encounter; prostitute.

Little mama: Short CB antenna.

Load: Cargo.

Load of postholes: Empty truck.

Local yokel: Local police.

Log some Z's: Get some sleep.

Long distance phone call ; Message for a specific CBer.

Loose boards (or) boardwalk: Rough road.

Lower flaps: Slow down.

LSB: Lower side band. 23 lowest-frequency channels in sideband CB set.

M

Magic City: Birmingham, Ala.

Magnolia State: Mississippi.

Mail: CB conversation. Example: "We be reading the mail."

Mama: Nine-foot CB antenna. Also, wife.

Mama bear: Policewoman.

Mama's lane: Passing lane on highway for truckers anxious to get home.

Mama Smokey: Policewoman.

Man, The: Policeman.

Man with a Gun: Policeman with radar.

Maniac: Truck mechanic:.

Marker: See "Mile marker."

Mayday: Emergency! Help me! "10-33"—see 10-Code.

Mercy: Mild exclamation: "Gee-golly-gosh; like wow."

Mercy sakes: Strong exclamation; substitute for four-letter words prohibited by FCC.

Metal: Floorboard; firewall. Example: "Put the pedal to the metal."

Metro: Three-wheeled motor-cycle used by city police.

Mexican overdrive: Neutral position in truck transmission; used for illegal coasting.

Mick-e-nick: Truck mechanic.

Mickey Mitchell (or Mouse): Local police.

Midnight overdrive: Same as "Mexican overdrive."

Mike fright: Hesitancy to speak, experienced by many new CBers. Also used to describe soft-spoken CBer.

Mile marker: Slender, numbered post on shoulder of interstate highway; used by many CBers to describe location.

Milford Land: Passing lane.

Milk run: Easy trip.

Mini-skirt: Girl.

Mini-State: Rhode Island.

Minnie: Small load or shipment, usually less than 100 pounds.

Mixing bowl: Complicated or cloverleaf intersection of highways.

Mixmaster: Same as "Mixing bowl."

Mobile eyeball: Visual check while moving. Example: "Mobile eyeball my mudflaps will you, good buddy?"

Mobile parking lot: Automobile carrier.

Mobile unit: Vehicle or person equipped with radio transreceiver, including CB.

Mobiling: Driving; going for a ride.

Moccasin: Linear amplifier.

Modulate: Talk.

Modulation booster: Device which increases sensitivity of microphone circuit in CB set without distortion.

Mollies: Sleep-preventing pills; "uppers."

Monford lane: Passing lane on highway.

Monitor: Listen without transmitting. Done especially on Channel 9, the emergency channel.

Monkey Town: Montgomery, Ala.

Monkey Ward: Montgomery Ward store.

Monster lane: Extreme left-hand lane of multi-lane highway.

Moonlight: Take back roads to avoid law enforcement officials.

Motion lotion: Fuel.

Motor City: Detroit, Mich.

Motoring: Driving; riding.

Motor mouth: Constant talker.

Mountie: Policeman in vehicle.

Movable parking deck (or lot): Automobile carrier. Also, "Movable" is same as "portable," as in "portable barnyard," etc.

M-20: Location; destination; meeting place.

Mud: Coffee.

Mud flaps: Rear of truck.

Muff: Woman.

Mule: Small tractor truck.

Muskrat: Child.

N

Nap trap: Rest area; motel.

Negatine: No.

Negative: No.

Negative contact: No answer.

Negative copy: Unable to understand.

Negative ground: Negative post on truck battery. Also cable from negative post to major metal component of truck. Electrical circuitry of nearly all trucks and CB sets has "negative" as opposed to "positive" ground.

Negator: No.

Negatory: No.

Nightcrawlers: Police all over the place.

Nine-to-fivers: Commuter traffic; day workers.

Ninety-weight: Liquor.

Nod out: Fall asleep.

Noise: Electronic interference.

Noise blanker: Minimizes interference from car electrical system; usually controlled by a sliding switch. Similar to "Automatic noise limiter" (see "ANL"), but works only on certain kinds of noise.

Noise limiter: Same as "noise blanker."

Nose dive: Trailer tipped forward.

O

Oil burner: Old truck or car.

Okie blower: Air scoop to cool engine compartment or provide ram air for mild power increase.

Old lady: Wife.

OM: Old man; husband.

Omnidirectional antenna: Antenna that radiates and receives approximately equally well in all directions.

One time: Quick question, answer or statement. "Breaker one time, what's your 20?" means, "Fast interruption, what is your location?" (See also 10-Code.)

On a ___ turn: Return portion of a round trip. Example: "We're on a Shaky City turn" means, "we're coming back from Los Angeles."

On standby: Monitoring; listening but not transmitting.

On the by: Same as "On standby."

On the move: In motion; driving.

On the peg: At the legal speed limit.

On the pin: Trailer is coupled to tractor truck.

On the side: Same as "On standby." Also, vehicle parked or on side of road.

Open season: Police are very active.

Other half: Spouse (usually wife).

Other radio: Radio in addition to CB, usually to monitor police calls.

Out: Transmission completed. No reply expected.

Outdoor TV: Drive-in movie.

Outrigger: Device to increase width of trailer.

Over: Finished talking; awaiting reply.

Over-modulation: Talking too much. Also, distortion resulting when speaker is too close to microphone or preamp microphone is turned too high.

Over the shoulder: The road behind.

OW: Old woman; old wife.

P

P and D: Local pickup and delivery truck.

Padiddle: Vehicle with one headlight out.

Padoodle: Same as "Padiddle."

Pair of buffalos: 55 miles per hour.

Pair of fives: Same as "Pair of buffalos."

Pair of nickels: Same as "Pair of buffalos."

Pair of sevens: No contact or answer. From "10-77" in 10-Code: "Negative contact."

Pajama wagon: Tractor truck with built-in sleeping compartment.

Pancake: Air brake· diaphragm.

Panic in the streets: FCC inspectors are checking area.

Panty-stretcher:
Broad-beamed woman. (Originally "handle" for a specific "Pavement princess.")

Papa bear: State trooper with CB equipment.

Paper: Speeding ticket.

Paper hanger: Police handing out speeding tickets.

Paperwork: Writing up speeding tickets. Example: "Smokey's doing his paperwork at marker 189."

Part 15: Portion of FCC Rules and Regulations applicable to operating low-power radio transmitters that need not be licensed.

Part 95: Part of FCC Rules and Regulations applicable to Citizens Radio Service (CB).

Pass the numbers: Wish the best.

Patch: City, town. Also, voice contact by linking radio and telephone.

Pay hole: High gear in truck transmission.

Pavement princess: Prostitute at truck stop.

PC: Printed circuit.

Peaked up: Tuned up; well adjusted.

Peak power: Maximum wattage on CB set.

Peanut butter ears: Inattentive; hard of hearing; not listening to CB.

Peanut wagon: Small tractor truck pulling big trailer.

Pedal: Move, drive, also, accelerator pedal.

Pedal along and wait: Drive slowly. Also, coast.

Pedal down: Drive fast.

Pedal slower: Slow down.

Pedal to the metal, put the: Slow down.

Peddle run: Door to door delivery.

Peel off: Make a turn; leave the highway.

Peg: Legal speed limit.

Peg leg: Truck with two rear axels, only one of which applies power to the wheels.

PEP: Peak envelope power; generated by modulated single sideband transmitter.

Persuader: Linear amplifier.

Pete: Peterbilt truck.

Peter Rabbit: Police (W).

Petro: Gasoline.

Petro refinery: Gasoline, fuel or oil truck.

PF flyers: Truck wheels.

Philly Town: Philadelphia, Pa.

Pick 'em up truck: Pickup truck.

Pickle suit: Marine uniform.

Pictures: Radar speed check. Example: "Smokey's takin' pictures."

Picture-taking machine. Radar speed reading device.

Piece of paper: Speeding ticket.

Pig: Policeman.

Pigeon: Vehicle caught speeding.

Piggyback: Trailer or cargo carried partway by rail. Also, trailer pulled by passenger car.

Piggy bank: Toll booth.

Pigtail: Cable to transmit electrical power from tractor to trailer.

Pike: Turnpike; toll road.

Pin: Safety device connecting tractor with trailer.

Pin up: Hook up tractor and trailer.

Pink panther: Police car with CB radio.

Pink QSL card: Warning ticket for speeding.

Pipe line: Specific CB channel. Example: "We'll monitor that 19 pipeline for you, good buddy."

Pit stop: Rest, meal or fuel stop.

Plain _____ wrapper: Unmarked police car, usually with color specified. Example: "Plain white wrapper at marker 27, and he's taking pictures."

Plucker: Euphemism for a four letter word.

Polack kids: Cattle.

Polack school bus: Cattle truck.

Polar bear: State trooper.

Polaroid: Police radar.

Pole cat: Black and white police car.

Poor devil: Newly wed.

Porky bear: Police of any kind.

Portable barnyard: Livestock truck or trailer.

Portable can: Trailer hauling any kind of liquid.

Portable chicken coop: Moveable weighing station.

Portable floor: Flatbed trailer.

Portable gas station: Gasoline tanker.

Portable parking lot: Automobile carrier.

Portable pipeline: Gas, milk or oil truck.

Portable stockyard: Cattle truck.

Portrait painter: Policeman making radar speed checks.

Positive: Yes.

Positive ground: Unusual setup for automotive electrical system or CB set. Opposite of "Negative ground."

Possum belly: Double-decker livestock hauler.

Post: Mile marker.

Post holes: Empty. Example: "We're on that Chi flip flop with a load of post holes" means, "I'm returning empty from Chicago."

Pots: Flares on highway to warn of hazard ahead.

Potty mouth: Obscene or foul-mouthed CBer.

Pound meter: S meter on CB set. Measures reception on scales of 1 to 10. See "S" meter.

Pounds: Numbers on S meter; each equals five decibels (dB).

Pour on coal: Apply power.

Power mike: Microphone with built-in preamplifier system for strong audio quality range.

Preamp: Same as "Power mike."

Pregnant roller skate: Volkswagen "Beetle."

Professional: Driver of a "Big rig."

Proud: Clear. Example. "We read you loud and proud."

PTT: Push-to-talk switch on CB microphone.

Pulling 'em down: Stopping truckers and motorists. Example: "Smokey's taking pictures and pulling 'em down."

Pull back: Slow down.

Pull in: Stop.

Pull the big switch: Shut off CB set.

Pull the pin: Release the lock between tractor and trailer.

Pull the plug: Same as "Pull the big switch."

Pump: Amplifier.

Pumpkin: Flat tire.

Pup: Short trailer.

Push: Drive. Example: "We're a professional. We push a rig for a living."

Put an eyeball on: See; look. Example: "Put an eyeball on them seat covers in that there white horse comin' at ya, good buddy.

Put it on the floor: Try for maximum speed. Example: "Put it on the floor and look for some more."

Put on air: Apply brakes.

Put on iron: Install tire chains.

Put yourself up here: Increase speed and join em; the road is clear ahead of you.

Put the hammer down: Full speed ahead.

Put the hammer in the tool box: Warning; slow down.

Putting out: Signal strength. Example: "You're putting out loud and proud, good buddy."

Q

Q Card: Post card acknowledging radio contract. See, "Wall paper."

Quasar: Girl; woman; female. From the TV commercial, "Works in a drawer."

Queen City: Cincinnati, O.; other cities as well.

Quick trip around the Horn: Tune rapidly through all 23 CB channels.

Quiz: Breath test by police to check on drinking drivers.

R

Radar Alley: Any stretch of highway that is locally notorious for radar, as US 90 in Ohio.

Raddiddio: Radio.

Radio check: Request for another CBer to report on quality of sender's signal. Also, request to test quality of sender's reception.

Rain locker: Shower room.

Rake the leaves: Look out for police in rear; job of "Back door" in CB convoy. Example: "Shake the trees and rake the leaves for Smokey."

Rascal: Friendly term; "buddy."

Ratchet jaw (or mouth): Talk. "Modulating," idle or excessive chatter.

Rally: Gathering of CBers; smaller than a "jamboree."

Rat race: Heavy traffic.

REACT: Radio Emergency Associated Citizens Teams; worthwhile association which monitors emergency Channel 9 to which many CBers belong.

Read: Understand; receive; hear; listen; "copy."

Rebound: Return trip; "flip."

Red wheel: Red light on police car (some states).

Reefer: Refrigerated truck or trailer.

Refinery: Gasoline truck or trailer.

Relocation consultant: Moving van.

REST: Radio Emergency Safety Teams to monitor emergency radio channels.

Rest-'em-up place: Rest area.

RF: Radio frequency, measured in cycles per second.

Rider: Vehicle without CB that is following one equipped with CB.

Riding shotgun: In passenger's seat; usually applied to trucker's partner or helper.

Rig: CB radio equipment; tractor-trailer unit.

Rip off: Steal; theft.

Rip strip: Expressway; freeway; highway.

Rizzo's Raiders: Police (Philadelphia, Pa.).

Road hog: Vehicle operator who uses more than his share of highway.

Road jockey: Truck or tractor-trailer driver; "professional."

Road tar: Coffee.

Rock: Crystal in CB set.

Rocking chair: Middle vehicle or vehicles in CB convoy between "front door" and "back door" who can relax and take things easy.

Rocks: Bricks; stones.

Roger: Yes; "Affirmative"; "10-4."

Roger Roller Skate: Speeder who is so far above speed limit that he is certain to get a ticket.

Roll 'n' rest: Drive and stop at regular intervals on long trip.

Roller skate: Subcompact car; Chevette, Datsun, etc.

Rolling: Moving; under way. Also, same as "movable" or "portable," as in "rolling" or "movable parking lot," etc.

Rolling bear: Police in moving vehicle.

Rolling roadblock: Slow-moving vehicle.

Rubber Duck: Lead vehicle in CB convoy. From recording, "Convoy."

Rubber neckers: Lookers; gawkers; especially at scene of an accident.

Rug rat: Small child.

Run interference: Drive fast in a car not equipped with CB that is likely to be caught by police.

Run out of road: Wreck.

Run out the front end: Vehicle at front of convoy gets beyond radio range of other vehicles in convoy.

Running barefoot: Operating CB set without linear amplifier. Also, operating CB set without FCC license.

Running shotgun: Same as "riding shotgun."

Running together: Comprising a CB convoy.

S

S and H: Money; "Green Stamps."

Saddle: One of middle vehicles in CB convoy; see "Rocking chair."

Saddle tanks: External fuel storage containers on both sides of truck or tractor.

Safer Shaffer: Shaffer Truck firm hauling refrigerated cargo.

Sailboat fuel: Out of gas.

Salt and pepper: Black and white police cars in some states.

Sale mines: One's place of employment.

Salt shaker: Truck that lays salt on roads.

San Quentin jail bait (or quail): Female under age of legal consent.

Say what?: Repeat; what did you say?

Scab: Ham radio operator's term for CBer.

Scab house: Weighing station.

Scanner receiver: Radio set that tunes itself to preselected channels or stations, stopping automatically when it picks up a signal and then tuning again for other signals when the one it has picked up disappears.

Scatter stick: Type of vertical CB antenna with ground plane.

Scratching: Vehicle moving at its best pace.

Seat cover: Pretty girl, especially one wearing skirt, in vehicle. Also, girl's legs.

Set it down: Stop quickly.

Set of doubles: Tractor-trailer; "Rig."

Seventy-threes: Best wishes; sign off.

Seventy-thirds: Same as "Seventy-threes."

Shag: Small trailer.

Shake the bushes: Check the road ahead for police or obstructions; what "Front door" in convoy does. Example: "Shake the bushes, Rubber Duck, We be rakin' the leaves."

Shake the lights: Blink headlights as warning to oncoming traffic.

Shaking the windows: Clear reception.

Shaky City (or Town): Los Angeles, Cal.

Shaky Side: West Coast, especially around Los Angeles, Cal.

Shamus: Policeman.

Shanty shaker: Tractor truck hauling mobile home.

Shark Town: Long Island, N.Y.

Sheep herder: Bad driver.

Shoat and goat conductor: Driver hauling cargo of live animals.

Shoes: Linear amplifier, boosting power illegally.

Shoes on: Top speed. Example: "We got our shoes in the monster lane." Also, using linear amplifier.

Shoot an eyeball: Take a look. Example: "Shot an eyeball at that superskirt in the pregnant roller skate."

Short short: Soon; in a little while.

Short skip: See "Skip."

Shotgun: Police radar device. Also, truck driver's partner or helper.

Shout: Call for specific person. Example: "Back door, this is Rubber Duck. Give us a shout."

Shovel coal: Apply power; accelerate.

Showoff lane: Passing lane.

Shy Town: Chicago; some as "Chi Town."

Sick horse: Tractor in poor condition; especially one low on power.

Sideband: Type of expensive CB set with 69 channels. Same as "SSB."

Side door: Passing lane.

Sin City: There are several leading candidates for this title.

Singing waffles: Radial-ply tires.

Six wheeler: Small truck. Also, passenger car pulling trailer.

Sixes and eights: Best regards; good luck.

Skating rink: Slippery road.

Ski: Same as "Skip"

Skins: Tires.

Skip: Radio signal bounced off inosphere; often received from distant transmitter, depending on special atmospheric conditions.

Skipper: CBer who communicates by means of skip signals.

Skip shooter: Same as "Skipper." Also, an illegal CB operator.

Skip talk: Radio signals reflected off inosphere; creates congestion for local CBers.

Skunk juice: Linear amplification.

Sky bear: Police in helicopter.

Slammer: Jail.

Slick: Clear; clean; okay.

Slicks sticks: Dual antennas.

Slop: Bad fuel.

Sloppy Joe: State trooper (in a few states).

S-meter: Instrument on CB radio that measures output in watts and input in decibels or "pounds." One "S" unit equals five dB. Range is from 1 to 10 "pounds," extremely weak to very strong signal.

Smile and comb your hair: Slow down; police radar ahead. Example: "Smile and comb your hair. Smokey's takin' pictures."

Smoke: Police; Smokey the Bear. Also, pass another vehicle quickly.

Smoke chopper: Police helicopter.

Smoke dope: Accelerate; drive fast.

Smoke 'em out: Drive slightly faster than speed limit to lure Smokey out of hiding, but not fast enough to get a speeding ticket.

Smoke-'em-up: Smokey the Bear.

Smoke (or Smokey) report: Identifying whearabouts of police.

Smoke screen: Police radar.

Smoke signals: Police in area.

Smoker: Smokey the Bear. Also, truck emitting heavy exhaust fumes.

Smokey, or Smokey the Bear: Police, especially state trooper. Named for bear wearing big hat, symbol of U.S. Forestry Service.

Smokey Beaver: Policewoman.

Smokey dozing: Police vehicle stopped or parked.

Smokey grazing: Police vehicle on median strip or shoulder of highway.

Smokey on grass: Same as "Smokey grazing."

Smokey on ground: Police out of car.

Smokey on rubber: Police vehicle moving.

Smokey on skates: Same as "Smokey on rubber."

Smokey on two-wheeler: Police on motorcycle.

Smokey with ears: Police vehicle equipped with CB radio.

SNAFU: Situation Normal; All Fouled Up.

Sneaky snake: Concealed police vehicle. Also, police vehicle equipped with CB radio.

Snooper: Spotlight on police car.

Snow bunny: Skier.

Snuff dipper: Prostitute at truck stop or roadside.

Snuffy Smith: Smith Transfer truck or driver.

Socks: Linear amplifier. Example: "You wearin' socks?"

Sparky: Electronics expert.

Splash on: Interfere with transmission. Same as "Step on."

Spoke: Speak; answer. Example: "Come on, Rubber Duck. Spoke to us."

Sport City: Any mecca for indoor or outdoor activities. Also, "Sin City."

Spread the greens: Distribute speeding tickets. Example: "Smokey's spreading the greens today."

Sprocket: Axle or transmission gear. Also, engine.

Spy in the Sky: Police helicopter.

Squealer: Tachograph; device to record engine speed.

S/RF meter: Instrument to measure relative strength of received and transmitted signals in some CB sets.

SSB: Single sideband ; type of expensive CB transmitter.

Stack them eights: Best regards.

Stage stop: Truck stop (W).

Starve the bears: Don't get a ticket.

Station license: Permission from FCC to operate more than one CB set on same license.

Steel City: Pittsburgh, Pa.

Steel man: Driver of tractor-trailer rig hauling steel.

Step on (or over): Interfere with transmission.

Step on Smokey's toes: Break the law.

Stepping: Moving right along; driving briskly.

Straight shot: Road ahead is free of obstructions and police. Same as "clear" or "clean shot."

Streaking: Cruising or high speed.

Struggling lane: Right-hand or slow lane of highway.

Struttin': Same as "Stepping."

Stuffy: Congested; heavy traffic.

Suds: Beer.

Suicide cargo: Dangerous load.

Suicide jockey: Driver of dangerous load.

Sunoco Special: Blue and yellow car of New York State trooper.

Superdome City: New Orleans, La.

Super skate: High performance car.

Super skirt: Either very pretty or very ugly girl.

Super slab: Wide concrete highway.

Super structure: Bridge.

Suppository: No; negative.

Swamper: Truck driver's helper.

Sweeping leaves: Bringing up rear of convoy; same as "back door" or "raking leaves."

Sweet thing: Female CBer.

Swindle sheet: Trucker's log.

Swinging beef: Cargo of beef sides on hooks in reefer truck or trailer.

SWR Meter: Standing Wave Ratio Meter for tuning antenna. Not permanent part of CB set.

Synthesizer: Feature in many CB sets which enables a few crystals to control a number of frequencies.

T

Tachograph: Device for recording engine speed. Same as "squealer," "tattle-tale."

Tailboard artist: Driver who shows off by following closely.

Tailgate: Follow too closely.

Take it to Channel ___: Switch to Channel ___.

Taking pictures: Police radar speed trap.

Taking pictures both ways: Police radar speed trap in both directions.

Talking skip: Long-distance CB communication. Same as "skip shooting."

Tall: Maximum vehicle height. Also, overhead clearance.

Tanker: Trailer carrying liquid.

Tar: Coffee.

Tattle-tale: Same as "Tachograph"; "squealer." Also, police helicopter.

Teddy Bear: Police.

Ten bye-bye: Sign off.

Ten Code: Shorthand means of verbal radio communication by numbers, where each number has a specific meaning both as question and answer. The most commonly-used Ten Codes are the abbreviated CB Ten Code for truckers, and the longer one used by police. Some commonly-used Ten Code expressions are given immediately below. Complete Truckers' CB and Police Codes are included in this book.

Ten four: Yes; affirmative; message received.

Ten fur: Same as "ten four."

Ten roger: Same as "ten four."

Ten ten: Stand by; standing by, signing off.

Ten twenty: Location.

Ten thirty-six: Time of day.

Ten-thirty-three: Emergency.

Ten 100: "I have to go to the bathroom."

Ten 102: "I am stopping for a beer."

Ten 400: "Drop dead."

Ten 1000: There's an FCC man around here.

Ten 2000: Dope pusher.

Ten pounds: Strong signal.

Tennis shoes: Truck tires.

Tense: Heavy traffic.

Texas strawberries: Shelled corn (W).

Thermos bottle: Tank truck; tanker.

Thick stuff: Fog.

Thirty-twelve: Emphatic affirmative; 10-4 three times.

Thirty-weight: Coffee.

Three-legged beaver: Male homosexual.

Threes: Salutation; either "hello" or "goodbye."

Threes and eights: Love and kisses; sign off.

Threes and nines: Salutation; sign off.

Threes on you: Best regards; sign off.

Thunder chicken: Ford Thunderbird.

Tiger in the tank: Linear amplifier.

Tijuana taxi: Conspicuously marked police car.

Tinsel City: Hollywood, Cal.

Toenails in radiator: Accelerator pedal to floor.

Toenails on front bumper: Same as "toenails in radiator."

Toilet mouth: User of foul language.

Tooling: Driving unhurriedly.

Top Twenty: National CB jamboree.

Torrible: Loud.

Town: Community of any size, large or small.

Tractor: Truck without a trailer: "Bob tail."

Trading stamps: Money.

Trailer trucking: Driving an 18-wheel rig.

Train station: Traffic court where fines are paid.

Training wheels: Learner's permit; temporary FCC license.

Trampoline: Bed.

Transmission: Gearbox in truck. Also, sending radio signal.

Transmission line: Coaxial cable connecting antenna to radio on CB rig.

Transporter: Truck; usually a large one.

Tricycle: Three-wheeled motorcycle.

Trick babe: Prostitute.

Tricky Dick's: San Clemente, Cal.

Trip: CB radio signal. Example: "How do we make the trip?" means "How do you read me?," or "How well do you receive my signal?"

Truck 'em easy: Drive safely.

Truck 'em up stop: Truck stop.

Truckin': Driving or riding in a truck.

Truckin' guy: Fellow truck driver; "good buddy."

Truckin' style: Same as "truckin'."

Truck jockey: Truck driver.

Truck stop commando: Swaggering truck driver.

Turkey: Ignorant or inept per-son; poor piece of equipment.

TVI: Television Interference.

Twelves: Other people present (from official Ten Code).

Twenty: Location. Example: "What's your twenty, Rubber Duck?"

Twin huskies: CB antennas mounted on both external rear view mirrors of truck cab.

Twin hustlers: Same as "twin huskies."

Twin mamas: Two nine-foot CB antennas.

Twisted pair: Telephone.

Twister: Highway inter-change.

Two tenners: Two antennas.

Two wheeler: Motorcycle.

TX: Telephone.

U

Uey: U-turn.

Ulcer: Traffic congestion.

Uncle Charlie: Federal Com-munications Commission. Also, "Charlie."

Unit: One of several CB sets covered by a CB station li-cense. See, "Station license."

Also, tractor-trailer, "rig."

Uppers: Sleep-preventing pills; "Mollies."

USB: Upper sideband; the 23 highest frequency channels in CB radio set.

USRC: United States Citizens Radio Council.

V

Van: Truck or trailer with enclosed cargo space.

Vitamins: Power; especially engine horsepower.

Vocal cords: CB transmitter.

Voice check: Radio check.

Volkswagen spotter: Convex truck mirror that magnifies images.

Vox: Voice-operated relay that activates transmitter circuits in CB radio; used in place of push-to-talk switch or "PTT" on microphone.

W

Walk on: Overpower weaker signal. Also, "walk over."

Walkie T: Walkie-talkie; small, portable transceiver.

Walkin': Driving.

Walkin' the dog: Strong transmission of signal, sometimes through use of linear amplifier.

Wallace lane: Middle lane on three-lane highway.

Wall paper: Post card acknowledging distant CB radio conversation, usually by a "skip shooter." Same as "Q cards" in ham radio.

Wall to wall: Good reception of CB radio signal. Example: "We read you wall to wall." Also, much or many of anything. Example: "Smokies are wall to wall."

Warden: Wife.

Watergate Town: Washington, D.C.

Wearing socks: Using linear amplifier.

We down: Transmission complete; sign off. Also, "We go"; "We gone"; "We went."

Weight watchers: Weighing station.

Welfare station: CB radio set purchased with welfare money.

West Coast mirrors: Large, external rear-view mirrors.

Western-style: Stale, especially coffee.

Whatever: Police; Smokey.

Wheeling: Driving.

White knight: State trooper.

White rabbit: Police.

White rabbit with ears: Police with CB.

Whomp: Interfere with transmission; "step on."

Wilco: Will comply; "ten four."

Willy Weaver: Drunk driver.

Wimp: Gutless or insignificant person.

Window washer: Heavy rain.

Windy City: Chicago, Ill.

Wood chuck: New driver on job.

Wooly bear: Policewoman; any woman.

Wolly wolly: Woman.

Working for moonlight express: Taking back roads to avoid weight stations.

Working man: Truck driver.

Work twenty: Place of employment.

Wrapper: Unmarked police car. Example: "Smokey's in a brown wrapper."

Wrinkle: Roughness; unevenness. Example: "Wrinkle in the pay hole" means truck is not running smoothly in high gear.

WT: Walkie Talkie; same as "Walkie T."

X

X-ray machine: Radar

XYD: Daughter.

XYL: Ex-young lady; old woman; wife. Also, "XY," "XYO."

XYM: Ex-young man; husband. Also, "XYN."

Y

Yap: Talk.

YL: Young lady.

Yo: Yes. Also, "Yoo."

Yo yo: Driver whose vehicle's speed is erratic.

You got it: Please answer; "over."

Your telephone is ringing: Another CBer is trying to contact you.

Z

Zap: Damage CB receiver of passing vehicle with powerful linear amplifier at close range.

Zephyr haul: Trip with light cargo.

Zoo: Police headquarters.

Z's: Sleep. Example: "We gonna cut some Z's."

CROSS REFERENCE

English to CB

This section is organized according to English equivalents of words most frequently used by truckers and other CBers. There are many shades of meaning in CB terminology. To find the exact term you want, first look up the English word here and then refer to the "CB to English" section of this Dictionary.

A

Accelerate: Drop hammer; foot on carburetor; jack it up; knock slack out; let it roll; pedal down; pedal to metal; put it on the floor; scratch; smoke dope; toenails in radiator.

Accident: Belly up; buy farm; buy orchard; greasy side up; run off (or out of) road.

Ambulance: Blood box; bone box.

AMC car: Kenosha Cadillac.

Animals, live: Go-go dancers; goat 'n' shoat; gump; Polack kids.

Answer: Come back; go ahead; go breaker; over; spoke.

Antenna: Beam type; fishing pole; hustler; big mama; little mama; omnidirectional; scatter stick; slick stick; twin huskies; hustlers or mamas; two tenners.

Atlanta, Ga.: Hotlanta; Hot Town.

B

Bed: Between sheets; coffin; wave maker; trampoline.

Beer: Brown bottle; brew; cold coffee; forty-weight; Kool Aid; suds; 10-102.

Birmingham, Ala.: Magic City.

Boston, Mass.: Bean Town.

Brakes: Binders; air; glad hands; jake.

Bridge: Haircut palace; super structure.

Bum: Junk buzzard; wimp.

Bus: Big dog; dog; blinkin' winkin'; kiddie car.

C

Cable (electrical): Pigtail.

Call: Holler; shout.

Car: Four wheeler; four by four (Jeep or similar four-wheel drive); rider (car without CB); roller skate (small); superskate (high performance).

Catch: Bag; catch a pigeon.

Cattle truck: Bull yard; Polack school bus.

CB operator: CBer; good buddy; gooney bird; peanut butter ears (inattentive); rascal; scab.

CB set: Bear buster; base station; ears; hillbilly music box; Japanese toy; rig; unit; welfare station.

Channel: Pipe line.

Channel 1: Basement.

Channel 9: Emergency.

Channel 15: Diesel digit.

Channel 19: Popular with CBers.

Chattanooga, Tenn.: Choo Choo Town.

Chevrolet truck: Detroit vibrator.

Chicago, Ill.: Chi; Shy Town; Windy City.

Child: Bubble gummer; forty-four; muskrat; rug rat; San Quentin quail; XYD.

Cigarettes: Cookies.

Cincinnati, O.: Queen City.

City: Patch; also, initial letter of city prefixed by word, "Big." Example: "Big T" is Tucson, Ariz. Or name of city with "Town" added, as in "Chi Town."

Closed: All right; gates shut.

Coffee: Bennie-chaser; black water; hot stuff; hundred-mile brew; mud; road tar; thirty-weight.

Control (lose): Hydroplane.

Convoy: Running together (group of CB-equipped vehicles). Has "front door," "Back door," "Rocking chair."

Corn (shelled): Texas strawberries.

Coupling (trailer): Fifth wheel; pin.

Crystals in CB set: Rocks; synthesizer.

D

Detroit, Mich.: Motor City.

Disneyland: Land of Disney (W).

Drinking: Willy Weaver (driver); quiz (breathalyzer test).

Drive (legally): Cruise; legalize; motor; on move; pedal along; tool; walk; wheel.

Drive (illegally): Boondock; stick foot in carburetor; moonlight; put pedal to metal; run interference; step on Smokey's toes; work for moonlight express.

Driver (good): Big rigger; concentrator; conductor; gear jammer; hard ankle; jockey; professional; pusher; shotgun or swamper (helper); steel man; working man.

Driver (bad): Bumper jumper; cowboy; Harvy Wallbanger; hog; hoo-hooer; sheep herder; tailboard artist; truck stop commando; turkey; yo yo.

Drugs: Bennies' California turn-arounds; cockleburrs; mollies; grass; shooting peanut butter; 10-2000; uppers.

E

East Coast: Dirty Side.

Emergency: Mayday.

Empty: Postholes (load); sailboat fuel (gas).

Engine: Peaked up (well tuned).

Engine cover: Doghouse; Okie blower (air scoop).

F

Fancy: Goodied up.

FCC inspector: Candy man; Charlie; Fed; panic in the streets; 10-1000.

Fire: Hot pants.

Fist fight: Knuckle buster.

Florida: Bikini State.

Fog: Ground cloud; thick stuff.

Ford car: Bird; horse; thunder chicken.

Ford truck: Fix or Repair Daily.

Forget it: Breeze it.

Fort Worth, Tex.: Cow Town.

Friend: Good buddy; cotton picker; guy; rascal.

Front: Breaking wind; front door.

Fuel: Go juice; motion lotion; petro; slop.

Fuel tanks: Saddle tanks.

G

Garage: Barn; hangar; junk yard; salt mine; work twenty.

Gasoline: Petro.

Gears and shifting: Creeper; down in corner; four-banger; granny; grab one; hole; kick down; Mexican or midnight overdrive; pay hole; sprocket.

GMC truck: Jimmy.

Goodbye: Adios; GBY; eighty-eights; seventy-threes; sixes and eights; stack them numbers; starve the bears; threes and eights (or nines); truck 'em easy.

H

Half ton: Bushel.

Hauling: Birdyback; expressway boogie; fat load; fishyback; peddle run.

Hear: Copy; read; receive.

Hearse: Bone box.

Hello: Threes; threes and nines.

Highway: Big slab; concrete jungle; loose boards (rough); parking lot; pike; rip strip.

Highway passing lane: Bullet; bumper; fifty-dollar; green stamp; left; mama's; monford; monster; showoff; side door; Wallace.

Hollywood, Cal.: Tinsel City.

Home: Port; twenty.

Homosexual: Three-legged beaver.

Houston, Tex.: Astrodome City.

Husband: Buffalo; OM; poor devil; XYM.

I

Ice: Skating rink.

Indianapolis, Ind.: Circle City.

Interference (radio): Blocking channel; button pushing; chucking carriers; dry carriers; goonie bird; keying mike; noise; TVI; whomping.

International Harvester truck: Corn binder.

Interrupt: Dust ears; let channel roll; one time; walk on; whomp.

Intersection: Mixmaster; twister.

J

Jail: Slammer.

K

Kentucky: Blue Grass State.

Kenworth truck: K-whopper.

L

Lane: See "Highway."

Las Vegas, Nev: Dice City.

Lead vehicle: Front door; front end; rubber duck; shake bushes.

Legal: Barefoot; legalized; light footing; on the peg.

Lights: Blinky; padiddle; candles; colors up; ditch light; fireworks; horse light; snooper.

Linear amplifier: After burner; big pump; hamburger helper; heater; moccasin; persuader; shoes; skunk juice; socks; tiger in tank. (See also, "Transmitter, illegal.").

Liquor: Cactus juice; ninety-weight.

Listen: Monitor; on standby; on the side.

Load: Minnie; fat; on the pin; pin up; post holes; suicide cargo; swinging beef; zephyr haul.

Look at: See "See."

Long Island, N.Y.: Shark Town.

Loud: Torrible.

Los Angeles, Cal.: Shaky City.

M

Mack truck: Bulldog.

Masturbate: Abuse it; choke chicken.

Marines: Green machine; pickle suit (uniform).

Meeting: Jamboree; coffee break; eyeball; rally; top twenty.

Message: Collect call; telephone is ringing.

Mile marker: Post.

Milwaukee, Wis.: Beer City.

Mirrors: Volkswagon spotters; West Coast mirrors.

Mississippi: Magnolia State.

Money: Green stamps; lettuce, S and H; trading stamps.

Montgomery, Ala.: Monkey Town.

Motorcycle: Evil Knievel; two wheeler; tricycle.

Mountain: Hump.

Moving: Rolling; on the move.

N

Nashville, Tenn.: Guitar Town.

New Jersey: Clean Side.

New Orleans, La.: Superdome City.

New York City: Big Apple; Dirty City; Fun City.

Nightclubbing: Boogieing.

No.: Double seven; negatine; negative; suppository.

O

Obscenity: Cotton picker (sometimes); finger wave; flake; mercy sakes (sometimes); funny book; latrine lips; plucker; potty mouth; 10-400; toilet mouth.

Ohio: Buckeye State.

Okay: 10-4; bring it on; clean and green; green light; knock it around; land of wonderful; put yourself up here.

Operator, CB: CBer; breaker.

Operator, female: Lady breaker; Goldilocks.

Operator, illegal: Apple; barefoot (without license); bootleg; dog walker; green CBer.

Over to you: Back; come on.

P

Parking lot (unpaved): Dirty floor.

Pennsylvania: Dirty Side (E).

Permission to speak: Break; breaker' broke.

Peterbilt truck: Pete.

Philadelphia, Pa.: Philly Town.

Pittsburgh, Pa.: Steel Town.

Place, location: Casa; twenty.

Plymouth Barracuda: 'Cuda; fish.

Police: Baby bear; bear; bearded buddy; big hat; boogie man; city kitty; county Mountie; Dudley Do-Right; electric teeth; girlie bear; jack rabbit; John Law; Johnny; Kodiak; Kohak; mama bear; the Man; Mickey Mitchell; Mountie; night crawler; papa bear; paper hanger; Peter Rabbit; pig; porky bear; Rizzo;s Raiders; Shamus; Sloppy Joe; Smoke 'em up; Smoker; Smokey; Smokey Bear; Smokey Beaver; Teddy Bear; Whatever; White Knight; white rabbit; woolly bear.

Police car: Bear on rubber; bear on skates; black and white; blue and white; blue light; brown bag; bubble gum machine; catch car; decoy; dummy; funny bunny; pink panther; pole cat; red wheel; rolling bear; salt and pepper; Smokey with ears; sneaky snake; Sunoco Special; Tijuana taxi; wrapper.

Police helicopter: Bear in the air (or sky); bird; chopper; eye (or spy) in the sky; sky bear; Smoke chopper; tattle-tale.

Police information: Bear report (or story); fix; Smokey report; Smokey dozing (or grazing or on rubber or ground).

Police station: Bear cage (or cave or den); slammer; train station; zoo.

Poultry truck: Cackle crate; chicken choker.

Power: Coal; horses; vitamins.

Promiscuity and prostitution: Bra buster; clean up; coffee break; dress for sale; hag bag; little bit; panty stretcher; pavement princess; snuff dipper; trick babe.

Q

R

Radar: Bear in bushes; bear trap; camera; fuzz buster; gun; Instamatic; Kodak; pictures; picture taking; Polaroid; portrait painting; shotgun; smoke screen; X-ray machine.

Radio: Raddiddio.

Radio terms: AF; AM; ALERT; FM; Part 15; Part 95; PEP; pounds; pre-amp; raddiddio, radio check; REACT; REST; "S" meter; scanner receiver; ski; skip; sideband; SRF; SWR; USB; USRC; voice check; vox.

Rain: Window washer.

Rear: Back door; back yard; donkey; hind end; mud flaps; over left shoulder; tail gate; raking leaves.

Reception (good): Bending windows; big ears; blowing

smoke; bodacious; breaking needle; coming in; five by five; hang it in your ear; hang needle; hit; nine pounds; proud; wall to wall.

Reception (bad): Break up; covered up; hash; negative copy; noise; pair of sevens; step on.

Repeat: Bring it back; come again; do it to me; say what.

Restaurant: Bean store; chew 'n' choke; choke 'em up stop.

Rest stop: Coke stop; 10-100; nap area or trap (motel); pit stop; rest 'em up; roll 'n' rest; stage stop; truck 'em up stop.

Return trip: Back side; back stroke; flip; rebound. (See also "Round Trip.")

Rhode Island: Mini-state.

Roadway truck: Big R.

Rookie: Baby bear; green apple; lid; training wheels; wood chuck.

Round trip: On a ＿ (name of city) turn; flip flop (See also "Return Trip.")

S

St. Louis, Mo.: Gateway City.

San Clemente, Cal.: Tricky Dick's.

San Diego, Cal.: Dago

San Francisco, Cal.: Hill Town.

See, Look at: Eyeball; lay an eye on.

Shaffer truck: Safer Shaffer.

Sign off: By; bye-bye; clear; down; eights; eighty-eights; final; gone; good (Or happy) numbers; have a 36-24-36; pass numbers; pull plug (or switch); seventy-threes; ten-bye; want.

Sleep: Between sheets; cut Z's; nod out.

Slow: Cool it; dead pedal; lower flaps; pedal slower; pedal up; pull back; put on air; put hammer in tool box; struggle.

Slow vehicle: Dead pedal; rolling road block; rubber necker.

Smith Transfer truck: Snuffy Smith.

Snow: Heavy stuff; fluff stuff.

Snyder truck: Big orange.

Soon: In a short short.

Speed limit: Double buffalo; double nickel; pair of fives; pair of nickels.

Speed trap: See "Radar."

Speeding: Blowing doors off; doin; it to it; dustin' britches; shoes on; smoking; smoking em out; stepping; streaking; strutting.

Speeding driver: Aviator; bear bait (or food or meat); flyboy; Roger Roller Skate.

Speeding ticket: Bear bite; bit on britches; blue slip; Christmas card; extra money; greens; green stamps; invitation; paper; pink slip, QSL card; stepping on Smokey's toes.

Standing by: Layin; an' stayin'; layin' over.

Stealing: Five finger discount; rip off.

Stolen: Gump; hoppins.

Stop transmitting: Back off; sign off; cut the co-ax; down; out; pull big switch; pull plug.

Stop vehicle: Anchor it; pull down; pull in; set it down.

Stuck: Downed; off (or on) the shoulder; on the side.

T

Tachograph: Squealer; tattletale.

Talk: Jaw jacking; modulation; yapping.

Talkative person: Alligator; bucket mouth; bull hauler (or jockey); diarrhea mouth; motor mouth; over-modulator; ratchet jaw.

Tampa, Fla.: Cigar City.

Telephone: Land line; LL; DX; patch (voice contact through CB set); twisted pair; TX.

Television: Boob tube.

Thank you: 10-4; GBY.

Tighten: Boom down.

Tire: Doughnut; pumpkin; rag (bad); skin; waffle.

Tire chains: Iron.

Tire, flat: Blown pumpkin; bubble trouble.

Toll booth: Piggy bank.

Tune: Trip; quick trip around Horn.

Tractor: Bob tail; cab; diesel car; fifth wheel; horse; mule; pajama wagon; peanut wagon; shag; shanty shaker; sick horse; turkey.

Tractor-trailer: Eighteen wheeler; semi; big rig; bogey; forty-footer; growed-up truck; set of doubles.

Traffic: Nine-to-fivers; rat race; stuffy; wall to wall; tense; ulcer.

Trailer: Circus wagon; city flyer; double bottom; out-rigger; portable barnyard, can, floor; parking lot; pipeline; petro refinery; piggybank; pup; tanker; possom belly; reefer; shag; thermos bottle.

Transmit: Hit; make trip; pick 'em up; put out; use vocal cords.

Transmitter, illegal: Foot warmer; heater; zap. (See also "Linear Amplifier.")

Trip: Milk run; flip flop (round).

Truck: Beer can; bottle popper; bucket of bolts; camel back; cement mixer; honey wagon; hopper body; iron; kidney buster; oil burner; P and D; pegleg; salt shaker; six wheeler; transporter van.

Truck, pickup: Country Cadillac; cowboy truck; hillbilly wagon; pick 'em up; put out.

Trucker's log: Bible; comic book, swindle sheet.

Tunnel: Hole in wall.

Turn: Bang; hang; jack it; peel off; uey.

U

Understand: Copy; read; roger; 10-4.

Unload: Break unit; drop body; pull pin.

V

Van, moving: Bedbug hauler; relocation consultants.

Van, small: Movable bedroom.

Volkswagon "Beetle": Pregnant roller skate.

W

Walkie Talkie: Walkie T; WT.

Warning: Beat bushes; brush your teeth and comb your hair; DDT (Don't Do That); honey on the road; open season; panic in the streets; pots; shake lights; smoke signals; twelves.

Wash: Douche job.

Washington, D.C.: Watergate Town.

Weighing station: Chicken coop; scab house; weight watchers.

West Coast: Shaky Side.

Wheels: PF flyers.

Wife: Better half; first sergeant; old lady; other half; OW; warden; XYL; XYO.

Woman: Beaver; bra buster; cover; fox; frilly blouse; Goldilocks; mini-skirt; muff; panty stretcher; quasar; seat cover; skirt; super skirt; sweet thing; woolly-woolly; YL.

Wrecker: Draggin' wagon.

X Y

Yes: Affirmative; forty-roger; for sure; four; guarantoya; positive; roger; 30-12; wilco; yo; yoo.

Z

Ten Codes

There are several Ten Codes, of which three are presented here. They are the Complete Code, the Abbreviated or CB Code, and the Law Enforcement Code. The purpose of all of them is to make radio messages clearly and briefly understood through a kind of verbal shorthand.

Local and professional variations in usage are unavoidable in all these Codes. Efforts at standardization have been made by several associations of radio users.

The Ten Codes included here are probably the most comprehensive available, and indicate usage that is generally agreed-upon across the country. The FCC Rules and Regulations require that, if you use a code, you must keep a copy of it at your CB set. The following pages of Ten Codes fill that requirement, so keep them handy!

In addition to Ten Codes, there are other codes with frivolous, funny and/or obscene meanings. Most of them are in the nature of "inside jokes," known to only a few people in a specific region or occupation.

Complete Ten Code

10–1	Receiving poorly.
10–2	Receiving well.
10–3	Stop transmitting.
10–4	Affirmative, message received.
10–5	Relay message.
10–6	Busy, please stand by.
10–7	Out of service, going off air.
10–8	In service, ready to receive calls.
10–9	Repeat the message.
10–10	Transmission completed, please stand by.
10–11	You're talking too rapidly.
10–12	I have visitors present.
10–13	Please advise about road and/or weather conditions.
10–14	Unassigned.
10–15	Unassigned.
10–16	Make a pick-up at _____.
10–17	Urgent business.
10–18	Do you have a message for me?
10–19	There is no message for you, return to base.
10–20	What's your location? (Or, My location is _____.)
10–21	Call by telephone.
10–22	Report in person to _____.
10–23	Stand by
10–24	I've completed my assignment.
10–25	Can you contact _____?
10–26	Disregard previous transmission.
10–27	I am moving to channel _____.
10–28	Please identify your station.
10–29	Your air-time limit is up.
10–30	Does not conform to FCC regulations.
10–31	Unassigned.
10–32	I will give you a radio check.
10–33	This station is carrying emergency traffic.

10–34	I'm having trouble, I need help.
10–35	Confidential information.
10–36	Correct time.
10–37	Wrecker needed at ___ ___.
10–38	Ambulance needed at _____.
10–39	Your message has been delivered.
10–40	Unassigned.
10–41	Please turn to channel _____.
10–42	There is accident at _____.
10–43	There is traffic congestion at _____.
10–44	I have a message for you.
10–45	All units, please report to base.
10–46	Assist motorist.
10–47 thru 10–49	Unassigned.
10–50	Break channel _____.
10–51 thru 10–59	Unassigned
10–60	Next message number is _____.
10–61	Unassigned.
10–62	I'm unable to understand you; use telephone.
10–63	Net directed to _____.
10–64	Net clear.
10–65	I am awaiting your next message/assignment.
10–66	Unassigned.
10–67	All units comply.
10–68	Unassigned
10–69	Message received.
10–70	There is a fire at _____.
10–71	Proceed with transmission in sequence.
10–72	Unassigned.
10–73	There is a speed trap set up at _____.
10–74	Negative.
10–75	You are causing interference.
10–76	Unassigned.

10–77	Negative contact.
10–78 thru 10–80	Unassigned
10–81	Reserve a hotel room for _____.
10–82	Reserve space for _____.
10–83	Unassigned.
10–84	My telephone number is _____.
10–85	My address is _____.
10–86 thru 10–88	Unassigned.
10–89	A radio repairman is needed at _____.
10–90	I have television interference.
10–91	Hold the microphone closer to your mouth.
10–92	Your transmitter is out of adjustment.
10–93	Check my frequency on this channel.
10–94	Please give me a long count.
10–95	Please transmit dead carrier for five seconds.
10–96	Unassigned.
10–97	Please check test signal.
10–98	Unassigned.
10–99	Mission completed, all units secure.
10–100	Time out for call of nature.
10–200	The police are needed at _____.

Note: Most of the 10-code signals can be used either as questions or as statements of fact.

Abbreviated or CB Ten Code

10–1	Signal is weak.
10–2	Signal is good.
10–3	Stop transmitting.
10–4	Acknowledgement; affirmative.
10–5	Relay message to _____.
10–6	Busy.
10–7	Out of service.
10–8	In service.
10–9	Repeat message.
10–10	Negative or no.
10–11	On duty.
10–12	Stand by or stop.
10–13	Weather or road report.
10–14	Message or information.
10–15	Message delivered.
10–16	Reply to message.
10–17	On the way.
10–18	Urgent.
10–19	In contact.
10–20	Location.
10–21	Call _____ by telephone.
10–22	Disregard.
10–23	Arrived at scene.
10–24	Assignment completed.
10–25	Report to or meet _____.
10–26	Estimated arrival time (ETA).
10–27	License or permit information.
10–28	Ownership information.
10–29	Check records.
10–30	Danger or caution.
10–31	Pick up.
10–32	Units needed.
10–33	Emergency. Need help fast.
10–34 or 10–36	Time

Law Enforcement Ten Code

10–0	Caution.
10–1	Unable copy—change location.
10–2	Signal good.
10–3	Stop transmitting.
10–4	Acknowledgement; yes.
10–5	Relay.
10–6	Busy—stand by unless urgent.
10–7	Out of service.
10–8	In service.
10–9	Repeat.
10–10	Fight in progress.
10–11	Dog case.
10–12	Stand by (Stop).
10–13	Weather—road report.
10–14	Prowler report.
10–15	Civil disturbance.
10–16	Domestic problem.
10–17	Meet complainant.
10–18	Complete assignment quickly.
10–19	Return to _____.
10–20	Location.
10–21	Call _____ by telephone.
10–22	Disregard.
10–23	Arrived at scene.
10–24	Assignment completed.
10–25	Report in person (meet) _____.
10–26	Detaining subject, expedite.
10–27	(Drivers) license information.
10–28	Vehicle registration information.
10–29	Check record for wanted.
10–30	Illegal use of radio.
10–31	Crime in progress.
10–32	Man with gun.

10–33	EMERGENCY
10–34	Riot.
10–35	Major crime alert.
10–36	Correct time.
10–37	(Investigate) suspicious vehicle.
10–38	Stopping suspicious vehicle.
10–39	Urgent—Use light, siren.
10–40	Silent run—no light, siren.
10–41	Beginning tour of duty.
10–42	Ending tour of duty.
10–43	Information.
10–44	Request permission to leave patrol _____ for _____.
10–45	Animal carcass in _____ lane at _____.
10–46	Assist motorist.
10–47	Emergency road repairs needed.
10–48	Traffic standard needs repairs at _____.
10–49	Traffic light out at _____.
10–50	Accident at _____.
10–51	Wrecker needed at _____.
10–52	Ambulance needed at _____.
10–53	Road blocked at _____.
10–54	Livestock on highway.
10–55	Intoxicated driver.
10–56	Intoxicated pedestrian.
10–57	Hit and run (PD) at _____.
10–58	Direct traffic at _____.
10–59	Convoy or escort.
10–60	Squad in vicinity.
10–61	Personnel in area.
10–62	Reply to message.
10–63	Prepare make written copy.
10–64	Message for local delivery.
10–65	Net message assignment.
10–66	Message cancellation.
10–67	Clear for net message.
10–68	Dispatch information.
10–69	Message received.

10–70	Fire alarm
10–71	Advise nature of fire.
10–72	Report progress on fire.
10–73	Smoke report.
10–74	Negative.
10–75	In contact with _____.
10–76	En route.
10–77	ETA (Estimated Time Arrival).
10–78	Need assistance.
10–79	Notify coroner.
10–80	Chase in progress.
10–81	Breatherlizer report.
10–82	Reserve lodging.
10–83	Work school crossing.
10–84	If meeting . . . advise time.
10–85	Delayed due to _____.
10–86	Officer/operator on duty.
10–87	Pickup/distribute checks.
10–88	Advise present telephone number of _____.
10–89	Bomb threat.
10–90	Bank alarm at _____.
10–91	Pick up prisoner/subject.
10–92	Improperly parked vehicle.
10–93	Blockade.
10–94	Drag racing.
10–95	Prisoner/subject in custody.
10–96	Mental subject.
10–97	Check (test) signal.
10–98	Prison/jail break.
10–99	Records indicate wanted or stolen.

International Phonetic Alphabet

Probably the most frequently-ignored FCC regulation is the one requiring CBers to identify themselves by call sign as well as "handle." Your call sign consists of three letters and four numbers assigned to you by the FCC. In giving your call letters, the regulation states that only a standard phonetic alphabet may be used.

There have been many changes in this alphabet since the "Able-Baker-Charlie" one you may have heard used on Late Show movies about World War II. No matter what section of the country—or the world, for that matter—you come from, this is the phonetic alphabet that is most universally understood.

Hotel Alpha Victor Echo Foxtrot Uniform November!

A.	Alpha	N.	November
B.	Bravo	O.	Oscar
C.	Charlie	P.	Papa
D.	Delta	Q.	Quebec
E.	Echo	R.	Romeo
F.	Foxtrot	S.	Sierra
G.	Golf	T.	Tango
H.	Hotel	U.	Uniform
I.	India	V.	Victor
J.	Juliette	W.	Whiskey
K.	Kilo	X.	X ray
L.	Lima	Y.	Yankee
M	Mike	Z.	Zulu

INEXPENSIVE "BEAR BUSTER"

CB Converter for AM Car Radio

Increasingly popular these days is a small electronic gadget, not much larger than two packs of cigarettes, called a CB converter. It is installed easily between your car antenna and AM radio, and receives but does not transmit on all 23 CB radio channels. Cost is usually in the $25 To $50 range, much less than a regular CB transceiver; no FCC license is required; with the "Bear Buster" turned off, you can use your car radio to receive AM commercial broadcasts as usual.

The following table will help you locate CB channels on your AM car radio dial.

CB CHANNEL	CB FREQ. IN Mz	RADIO DIAL NO.	CB CHANNEL	CB FREQ. IN Mz	RADIO DIAL NO.
1	26.965	1360	13	27.115	1510
2	26.975	1370	14	27.125	1520
3	26.985	1380	15	27.135	1530
4	27.005	1400	16	27.155	1550
5	27.015	1410	17	27.165	1560
6	27.025	1420	18	27.175	1570
7	27.035	1430	19	27.185	1580
8	27.055	1450	20	27.205	1600
9	27.065	1460	21	27.215	1610
10	27.075	1470	22	27.225	1620
11	27.085	1480	23	27.225	1650
12	27.105	1500			

Q-SIGNALS

Q-signals originated in the military and over the years amateur radio operators modified it when they adopted it. CBers made additional changes for their own usage.

The Q-signals listed are terms most likely heard on CB bands and the definitions are the most commonly understood meanings.

QRM—Interference from other stations transmitting on the same frequency.
QRN—Interference from man-made or natural sources.
QRP—Very low power rig.
QRT—Shut down the station.
QRU—Listening for messages directed to station.
QRV—Ready to take message.
QRX—Wait.
QRX1—Wait a minute.
QRZ—What station is calling.
QSB—Fading signals.
QSL—Wallpaper.
QSO—Conversation between stations.
QSY—Change channels.
QTH—Location of home station.

CURRENT AND OFFICIAL CB RADIO

RULES AND REGULATIONS

from the

FEDERAL COMMUNICATIONS COMMISSION

Part 95: Citizens Radio Service. Must be kept at your CB radio station.

SUBPART A—GENERAL

§ 95.1 Basis and purpose

The rules and regulations set forth in this part are issued pursuant to the provisions of Title III of the Communications Act of 1934, as amended, which vests authority in the Federal Communications Commission to regulate radio transmissions and to issue licenses for radio stations. These rules are designed to provide for private short-distance radiocommunications service for the business or personal activities of licensees, for radio signaling, for the control of remote objects or devices by means of radio; all to the extent that these users are not specifically prohibited in this part. They also provide for procedures whereby manufacturers of radio equipment to be used or operated in the Citizens Radio Service may obtain type acceptance and/or type approval of such equipment as may be appropriate.

§ 95.3 Definitions.

For the purpose of this part, the following definitions shall be applicable. For other definitions, refer to Part 2 of this chapter.

(a) Definitions of services.

Citizens Radio Service. A radiocommunications service of fixed, land, and mobile stations intended for short-distance personal or business radiocommunications, radio signaling, and control of remote objects or devices by radio; all to the extent that these uses are not specifically prohibited in this part.

Fixed service. A service of radiocommunication between specified fixed points.

Mobile *service.* A service of radiocommunication between mobile and land stations or between mobile stations.

(b) Definitions of stations.

Base station. A land station in the land mobile service carrying on a service with land mobile stations.

Class A station. A station in the Citizens Radio Service licensed to be operated on an assigned frequency in the 460—470 MHz band with a transmitter output power of not more than 50 watts.

Class B station. (All operations terminated as of November 1, 1971.)

Class C station. A station in the Citizens Radio Service licensed to be operated on an authorized frequency in the 26.96-27.23 MHz band, or on the frequency 27.255 MHz, for the control of remote objects or devices by radio, or for the remote actuation of devices which are used solely as a means of attracting attention, or on an authorized frequency in the 72-76 MHz band for the radio control of models used for hobby purposes only.

Class D station. A station in the Citizens Radio Service licensed to be operated for radiotelephony, only, on an authorized frequency in the 26.96-27.23 MHz band and on the frequency 27.255 MHz.

Fixed station. A station in the fixed service.

Land station. A station in the mobile service not intended for operation while in motion. (Of the various types of land stations, only the base station is pertinent to this part.)

Mobile station. A station in the mobile service intended to be used while in motion or during halts at unspecified points. (For the purposes of this part, the term includes hand-carried and pack-carried units.)

(c) Miscellaneous definitions.

Antenna structures. The term "antenna structures" includes the radiating system, its supporting structures and any appurtenances mounted thereon.

Assigned frequency. The frequency appearing on a station authorization from which the carrier frequency may deviate by an amount not to exceed that permitted by the frequency tolerance.

Authorized bandwidth. The maximum permissible bandwidth for the particular emission used. This shall be the occupied bandwidth or necessary bandwidth, whichever is greater.

Carrier power. The average power at the output terminals of a transmitter (other than a transmitter having a suppressed, reduced or controlled carrier) during one radio frequency cycle under conditions of no modulation.

Control point. A control point is an operating position which is under the control and supervision of the licensee, at which a person immediately responsible for the proper operation of the transmitter is stationed, and at which adequate means are available to aurally monitor all transmissions and to render the transmitter inoperative.

Dispatch point. A dispatch point is any position from which messages may be transmitted under the supervision of the person at a control point.

Double sideband emission. An emission in which both upper and lower sidebands resulting from the modulation of a particular carrier are transmitted. The carrier, or a portion thereof, also may be present in the emission.

External radio frequency power amplifiers. As defined in§ 2.815 (a) and as used in this part, an external radio frequency power amplifier is any device which, (1) when used in conjunction with a radio transmitter as a signal source is capable of amplification of that signal, and (2) is not an integral part of a radio transmitter as manufactured.

Harmful interference. Any emission, radiation or induction which endangers the functioning of a radionavigation service or other safety service or seriously degrades, obstructs or repeatedly interrupts a radio-communication service operating in accordance with applicable laws, treaties, and regulations.

Man-made structure. Any construction other than a tower, mast or pole.

Mean power. The power at the output terminals of a transmitter during normal operation, averaged over a time sufficiently long compared with the period of the lowest frequency encountered in the modulation. A time of 1/10 second during which the mean power is greatest will be selected normally.

Necessary bandwidth. For a given class of emission, the minimum value of the occupied bandwidth sufficient to ensure the transmission of information at the rate and with the quality required for the system employed, under specified conditions. Emissions useful for the good functioning of the receiving equipment, as for example, the emission corresponding to the carrier of reduced carrier systems, shall be included in the necessary bandwidth.

Occupied bandwidth. The frequency bandwidth such that, below its lower and above its upper frequency limits, the mean powers radiated are each equal to 0.5% of the total mean power radiated by a given emission.

Omnidirectional antenna. An antenna designed so the maximum radiation in any horizontal direction is within 3 dB of the minimum radiation in any horizontal direction.

Peak envelope power. The average power at the output terminals of a transmitter during one radio frequency cycle at the highest crest of the modulation envelope, taken under conditions of normal operation.

Person. The term "person" includes an individual, partnership, association, joint-stock company, trust or corporation.

Remote control. The term "remote control" when applied to the use or operation of a citizens radio station means control of the transmitting equipment of that station from any place other than the location of the transmitting equipment, except that direct mechanical control or direct electrical control by wired connections of transmitting equipment from some other point on the same premisis, craft or vehicle shall not be considered to be remote control.

Single sideband emission. An emission in which only one sideband is transmitted. The carrier, or a portion thereof, also may be present in the emission.

Station authorization. Any construction permit, license, or special temporary authorization issued by the Commission.

§ 95.5 Policy governing the assignment of frequencies.

(a) The frequencies which may be assigned to Class A stations in the Citizens Radio Service, and the frequencies which are available for use by Class C or Class D stations are listed in Subpart C of this part. Each frequency available for assignment to, or use by, stations in this service is available on a shared basis only, and will not be assigned for the exclusive use of any one applicant; however, the use of a particular frequency may be restricted to (or in) one or more specified geographical areas.

(b) In no case will more than one frequency be assigned to Class A stations for the use of a single applicant in any given area until it has been demonstrated conclusively to the Commission that the assignment of an additional frequency is essential to the operation proposed.

(c) All applicants and licensees in this service shall cooperate in the selection and use of the frequencies assigned or authorized, in order to minimize interference and thereby obtain the most effective use of the authorized facilities.

(d) Simultaneous operaion on more than one frequency in the 71–76 MHz band by a transmitter or transmitters of a single licensee is prohibited whenever such operation will cause harmful interference to the operation of other licensees in this service.

§ 95.6 Types of operation authorized.

(a) Class A stations may be authorized as mobile stations, as base stations, as fixed stations, or as base or fixed stations to be operated at unspecified or temporary locations.

(b) Class C and Class D stations are authorized as mobile stations only; however, they may be operated at fixed locations in accordance with other provisions of this part.

§ 95.7 General citizenship requirements.

A station license shall not be granted to or held by a foreign government or a representative thereof.

[§ 95.7 revised eff. 2-5-75; VI (75)-1]

SUBPART B

APPLICATIONS AND LICENSES

§ 95.11 Station authorization required.

No radio station shall be operated in the Citizens Radio Service except under and in accordance with an authorization granted by the Federal Communications Commission.

§ 95.13 Eligibility for station license.

(a) Subject to the general restrictions of § 95.7, any person is eligible to hold an authorization to operate a station in the Citizens Radio Service: *Provided,* That if an applicant for a Class A or Class D station authorization is an individual or partnership, such individual or each partner is eighteen or more years of age; or if an applicant for a Class C station authorization is an individual or partnership, such individual or each partner is twelve or more years of age. An unincorporated association, when licensed under the provisions of this paragraph, may upon specific prior approval of the Commission provide radiocommunications for its members.

NOTE: While the basis of eligibility in this service includes any state, territorial, or local governmental entity, or any agency operating by the authority of such governmental entity, including any duly authorized state, territorial, or local civil defense agency, it should be noted that the frequencies available to stations in this service are shared without distinction between all licensees and that no protection is afforded to the communications of any station in this service from interference which may be caused by the authorized operation of other licensed stations.

(b) [Reserved]

(c) No person shall hold more than one Class C and one Class D station license.

§ 95.14 Mailing address furnished by licensee.

Each application shall set forth and each licensee shall furnish the Commission with an address in the United States to be used by the Commission in serving documents or directing correspondence to that licensee. Unless any licensee advises the Commission to the contrary, the address contained in the licensee's most recent application will be used by the Commission for this purpose.

[§ *95.14 added new eff. 2-5-75; VI (75)-1]*

§ 95.15 Filing of applications.

(a) To assure that necessary information is supplied in a consistent manner by all persons, standard forms are prescribed for use in connection with the majority of applications and reports submitted for Commission consideration. Standard numbered forms applicable to the Citizens Radio Service are discussed in § 95.19 and may be obtained from the Washington, D.C., 20554, office of the Commission, or from any of its engineering field offices.

(b) All formal applications for Class C or Class D new, modified, or renewal station authorizations shall be submitted to the Commission's office at 334 York Street Gettysburg, Pa. 17325. Applications for Class A station authorizations, applications for consent to transfer of control of a corporation holding any citizens radio station authorization, requests for special temporary authority or other special requests, and correspondence relating to an application for any class citizens radio station authorization shall be submitted to the Commission's Office at Washington, D.C. 20554, and should be directed to the attention of the Secretary. Beginning January 1, 1973, applicants for Class A stations in the Chicago Regional Area, defined in § 95.19, shall submit their applications to the Commission's Chicago Regional Office. The address of the Regional Office will be announced at a later date. Applications involving Class A or Class D station equipment which is neither type approved nor cyrstal controlled, whether of commercial or home construction, shall be accompanied by supplemental data describing in detail the design and construction of the transmitter and methods employed in testing· it to determine compliance with the technical requirements set forth in Subpart C of this part.

(c) Unless otherwise specified, an application shall be filed at least 60 days prior to the date on which it is desired that Commission action thereon be completed. In any case where the applicant has made timely and sufficient application for renewal of license, in accordance with the Commission's rules, no license with reference to any activity of a continuing nature shall expire until such application shall have been finally determined.

(d) Failure on the part of the applicant to provide all the information required by the application form, or to supply the necessary exhibits or supplementary statements may constitute a defect in the application.

(e) Applicants proposing to construct a radio station on a site located on land under the jurisdiction of the U.S. Forest Service, U.S. Department of Agriculture, or the Bureau of Land Management, U.S. Department of the Interior, must supply the information and must follow the procedure prescribed by § 1.70 of this chapter.

§ 95.17 Who may sign applications.

(a) Except as provided in paragraph (b) of this section, applications, amendments thereto, and related statements of fact required by the Commission shall be personally signed by the applicant, if the applicant is an individual; by one of the partners, if the applicant is a partnership; by an officer, if the applicant is a corporation; or by a member who is an officer, if the applicant is an unincorporated association. Applications, amendments, and related statements of fact filed on behalf of eligible government entities, such as states and territories of the United States and political subdivisions thereof, the District of Columbia, and units of local government, including incorporated municipalities, shall be signed by such duly elected or appointed officials as may be competent to do so under the laws of the applicable jurisdiction.

(b) Applications, amendments thereto, and related statements of fact required by the Commission may be signed by the applicant's attorney in case of the applicant's physical disability or of his absence from the United States. The attorney shall in that event separately set forth the reason why the application is not signed by the applicant. In addition, if any matter is stated on the basis of the attorney's belief only (rather than his knowledge), he shall separately set forth his reasons for believing that such statements are true.

(c) Only the original of applications, amendments, or related statements of fact need be signed; copies may be conformed.

(d) Applications, amendments, and related statements of fact need not be signed under oath. Willful false statements made therein, however, are punishable by fine and imprisonment. U.S. Code, Title 18, section 1001, and by appropriate administrative sanctions, including revocation of station license pursuant to section 312 (a) (1) of the Communications Act of 1934, as amended.

§ 95.19 Standard forms to be used.

(a) *FCC Form 505, Application for Class C or D Station License in theCitizens Radio Service.* This form shall be used when:

(1) Application is made for a new Class C or Class D authorization. A separate application shall be submitted for each proposed class of station.

(2) Application is made for modicication of any existing Class C or Class D station authorization in those cases where prior Commission approval of certain changes is required (see § 95.35).

(3) Application is made for renewal of an existing Class C or Class D station authorization, or for rein-statement of such an expired authorization.

(b) *FCC Form 400, Application for Radio Station Authorization in the Safety and Special Radio Services.* Except as provided in paragraph (d) of this section, this form shall be used when:

(1) Application is made for a new Class A base station or fixed station authorization. Separate applications shall be submitted for each proposed base or fixed station at different fixed locations; however, all equipment intended to be operated at a single fixed location is considered to be one station which may, if necessary, be classed as both a base station and a fixed station.

(2) Application is made for a new Class A station authorization for any required number of mobile units (including hand-carried and pack-carried units) to be operated as a group in a single radiocommunication system in a particular area. An application for Class A mobile station authorization may be combined with the application for a single Class A base station au-

thorization when such mobile units are to be operated with that base station only.

(3) Application is made for station license of any Class A base station or fixed station upon completion of construction or installation in accordance with the terms and conditions set forth in any construction permit required to be issued for that station, or application for extension of time within which to construct such a station.

(4) Application is made for modification of any existing Class A station authorization in those cases where prior Commission approval of certain changes is required (see § 95.35).

(5) Application is made for renewal of an existing Class A station authorization, or for reinstatement of such an expired authorization.

(6) Each applicant in the Safety and Special Radio Services (1) for modification of a station license involving a site change or a substantial increase in tower height or (2) for a license for a new station must, before commencing construction, supply the environmental information, where required, and must follow the procedure prescribed by Subpart I of Part 1 of this chapter (§§ 1.1301 through 1.1319) unless Commission action authorizing such construction would be a minor action with the meaning of Subpart I of Part 1.

(7) Application is made for an authorization for a new Class A base or fixed station to be operated at unspecified or temporary locations. When one or more individual transmitters are each intended to be operated as a base station or as a fixed station at unspecified or temporary locations for indeterminte periods, such transmitters may be considered to comprise a single station intended to be operated at temporary locations. The application shall specify the general geographic area within which the operateon will be confined. Sufficient data must be

submitted to show the need for the proposed area of operation.

(c) *FCC Form 703, Application for Consent to Transfer of Control of Corporation Holding Construction Permit or Station License.* This form shall be used when application is made for consent to transfer control of a corporation holding any citizens radio station authorization.

(d) Beginning April 1, 1972, FCC Form 425 shall be used in lieu of FCC Form 400, applicants for Class A stations located in the Chicago Regional Area defined to consist of the counties listed below:

ILLINOIS

1. Boone.	28. Livingston.
2. Bureau.	29. Logan.
3. Carroll.	30. Macon.
4. Champaign.	31. Marshall.
5. Christian.	32. Mason.
6. Clark.	33. McHenry.
7. Coles.	34. McLean.
8. Cook.	35. Menard.
9. Cumberland.	36. Mercer.
10. De Kalb.	37. Moultrie.
11. De Witt.	38. Ogle.
12. Douglas.	39. Peoria.
13. Du Page.	40. Piatt.
14. Edgar.	41. Putnam.
15. Ford.	42. Rock Island.
16. Fulton.	43. Sangamon.
17. Grundy.	44. Shelby.
18. Henry.	45. Stark.
19. Iroquois.	46. Stephenson.
20. Jo Daviess.	47. Tazewell.
21. Kane.	48. Vermilion.
22. Kankakee.	49. Warren.
23. Kendall.	50. Whiteside.
24. Knox.	51. Will.
25. Lake.	52. Winnebago.
26. La Salle.	53. Woodford.
27. Lee	

INDIANA

1. Adams.	28. Madison.
2. Allen.	29. Marion.
3. Benton.	30. Marshall.
4. Blackford.	31. Miami.
5. Boone.	32. Montgomery.
6. Carroll.	33. Morgan.
7. Cass.	34. Newton.
8. Clay.	35. Noble.
9. Clinton.	36. Owen.
10. De Kalb.	37. Parke.
11. Delaware.	38. Porter.
12. Elkhart.	39. Pulaski.
13. Fountain.	40. Putnam.
14. Fulton.	41. Randolph.
15. Grant.	42. St. Joseph.
16. Hamilton.	43. Starke.
17. Hancock.	44. Steuben.
18. Hendricks.	45. Tippecanoe.
19. Henry.	46. Tipton.
20. Howard.	47. Vermilion.
21. Huntington.	48. Vigo.
22. Jasper.	49. Wabash.
23. Jay.	50. Warren.
24. Kosciusko.	51. Wells.
25. Lake.	52. White.
26. Lagrange.	53. Whitley.
27. La Porte.	

IOWA

1. Cedar.	5. Jones.
2. Clinton.	6. Muscatine.
3. Dubuque.	7. Scott.
4. Jackson.	

MICHIGAN

1. Allegan.	13. Kalamazoo.
2. Barry.	14. Kent.
3. Berrien.	15. Lake.
4. Branch.	16. Mason.
5. Calhoun.	17. Mecosta.
6. Cass.	18. Montcalm.
7. Clinton.	19. Muskegon.
8. Eaton.	20. Newaygo.
9. Hillsdale.	21. Oceana.
10. Ingham.	22. Ottawa.
11. Ionia.	23. St. Joseph.
12. Jackson.	24. Van Buren.

96

OHIO

1. Defiance.	4. Van Wert.
2. Mercer.	5. Williams.
3. Paulding.	

WISCONSIN

1. Adams.	18. Manitowoc.
2. Brownn.	19. Marquette.
3. Calumet.	20. Milwaukee.
4. Columbia.	21. Outagamie.
5. Dane.	22. Ozaukee.
6. Dodge.	23. Racine.
7. Door.	24. Richland.
8. Fond du Lac.	25. Rock.
9. Grant.	26. Suak.
10. Green.	27. Sheboygan.
11. Green Lake.	28. Walworth.
12. Iowa.	29. Washington.
13. Jefferson.	30. Waukesha.
14. Juneau.	31. Waupaca.
15. Kenosha.	32. Waushara.
16. Kewaunee.	33. Winnebago.
17. Lafayette.	

§ 95.25 Amendment or dismissal of application.

(a) Any application may be amended upon request of the applicant as a matter of right prior to the time the application is granted or designated for hearing. Each amendment to an application shall be signed and submitted in the same manner and with the same number of copies as required for the original application.

(b) Any application may, upon written request signed by the applicant or his attorney, be dismissed without prejudice as a matter of right prior to the time the application is granted or designated for hearing.

§ 95.27 Transfer of license prohibited.

A station authorization in the Citizens Radio Service may not be transferred or assigned. In lieu of such transfer or assignment, an application for new station authorization shall be filed in each case, and the previous authorization shall be forwarded to the Commission for cancellation.

§ 95.29 Defective applications.

(a) If an applicant is requested by the Commission to file any documents or information not included in the prescribed application form, a failure to comply with such request will constitute a defect in the application.

(b) When an application is considered to be incomplete or defective, such application is considered to be incomplete or defective, such application will be returned to the applicant, unless the Commission may otherwise direct. The reason for return of the applications will be indicated, and if appropriate, necessary additions or corrections will be suggested.

§ 95.31 Partial grant.

Where the Commission, without a hearing, grants an application in part, or with any privileges, terms, or conditions or other than those requested , the action of the Commission shall be considered as a grant of such application unless the applicant shall, within 30 days from the date on which such grant is made, or from its effective date if a later date is specified, file with the Commission a written rejection of the grant as made. Upon receipt of such rejection, the Commission will vacate its original action upon the application and, if appropriate, set the application for hearing.

§ 95.33 License term.

Licenses for stations in the Citizens Radio Service will normally be issued for a term of 5 years from the date of original issuance, major modification, or renewal.

§ 95.35 Changes in transmitters and authorized stations.

Authority for certain changes in transmitters and authorized stations must be obtained from the Commission before the changes are made, while other changes do not require prior Commission approval. The following paragraphs of this section describe the conditions under which prior Commission approval is or is not necessary.

(a) Proposed changes which will result in operation inconsistent with any of the terms of the current authorization require that an application for modification of license be submitted to the Commission. Application for modification shall be submitted in the same manner as an application for a new station license, and the licensee shall forward his existing authorization to the Commission for cancellation immediately upon receipt of the superseding authorization. Any of the following changes to authorized stations may be made only upon approval by the Commission:

(1) Increase the overall number of transmitters authorized.

(2) Change the presently authorized location of a Class A fixed or base station or control point.

(3) Move, change the height of, or erect a Class A station antenna structure.

(4) Make any change in the type of emission or any increase in bandwidth of emission or power of a Class A station.

(5) Addition or deletion of control point(s) for an authorized transmitter of a Class A station.

(6) Change or increase the area of operation of a Class A mobile station or a Class A base or fixed station authorized to be operated at temporary locations.

(7) Change the operating frequency of a Class A station.

(b) When the name of a licensee is changed (without changes in the ownership, control, or corporate structure), or when the mailing address of the licensee is changed (without changing the authorized location of the base or fixed Class A station) a formal application for modification of the license is not required. However, the licensee shall notify the Commission promptly of these changes. The notice, which may be in letter form, shall contain the name and address of the licensee as they appear in the Commission's records, the new name and/or address, as the case may be, and the call signs and classes of all radio stations authorized to the licensee under this part. The notice concerning Class C or D radio stations shall be sent to Federal Communications Commission, Gettysburg, Pa. 17325, and a copy shall be maintained with the records of the station. The notice concerning Class A stations shall be sent to (1) Secretary, Federal Communications Commission, Washington, D.C. 20554, and (2) to Engineer in Charge of the Radio District in which the station is located, and a copy shall be maintained with the license of the station until a new license is issued.

(c) Proposed changes which will not depart from any of the terms of the outstanding authorization for the station may be made without prior Commission approval. Included in such changes is the substitution of transmitting equipment at any station, provided that the equipment employed is included in the Commission's "Radio Equipment List," and is listed as acceptable for use in the appropriate class of station in this service. Provided it is crystal-controlled and otherwise complies with the power, frequency tolerance, emission and modulation percentage limitations prescribed, nontype accepted equipment may be substituted at:

(1) Class C stations operated on fre-

quencies in the 26.99-27.26 MHz band;

(2) Class D stations until November 22, 1974.

(d) Transmitting equipment type accepted for use in Class D stations shall not be modified by the user. Changes which are specifically prohibited include:

(1) Internal or external connection or addition of any part, device or accessory not included by the manufacturer with the transmitter for its type acceptance. This shall not prohibit the external connection of antennas or antenna transmission lines, antenna switches, passive networks for coupling transmission lines or antennas to transmitters, or replacement of microphones.

(2) Modification in any way not specified by the transmitter manufacturer and not approved by the Commission.

(3) Replacement of any transmitter part by a part having different electrical characteristics and ratings from that replaced unless such part is specified as a replacement by the transmitter manufacturer.

(4) Substitution or addition of any transmitter oscillator crystal unless the crystal manufacturer or transmitter manufacturer has made an express determination that the crystal type, as installed in the specific transmitter type, will provide that transmitter type with the capability of operating within the frequency tolerance specified in Section 95.45 (a).

(5) Addition or substitution of any component, crystal or combination of crystals, or any other alternation to enable transmission on any frequency not authorized for use by the licensee.

(e) Only the manufacturer of the particular unit of equipment type accepted for use in Class D stations may make the permissive changes allowed under the provisions of Part 2 of this chapter for type acceptance. However, the manufacturer shall not make any of the following changes to the transmitter without prior written authorization from the Commission:

(1) Addition of any accessory or device not specified in the application for type acceptance and approved by the Commission in granting said type acceptance.

(2) Addition of any switch, control or external connection.

(3) Modification to provide capability for an additional number of transmitting frequencies.

§ 95.37 Limitations on antenna structures.

(a) Except as provided in paragraph (b) of this section, an antenna for a Class A station which exceeds the following height limitations may not be erected or used unless notice has been filed with both the FAA on FAA Form 7460-1 and with the Commission on Form 714 or on the license application form, and prior approval by the Commission has been obtained for:

(1) Any construction or alteration of more than 200 feet in height above ground level at its site (§ 17.7 (a) of this chapter).

(2) Any construction or alteration of greater height than an imaginary surface extending outward and upward at one of the following slopes (§ 17.7 (b) of this chapter):

(i) 100 to 1 for a horizontal distance of 20,000 feet from the nearest point of the nearest runway of each airport with at least one runway more than 3,200 feet in length, excluding heliports, and seaplane bases without specified boundaries, if that airport is either listed in the Airport Directory of the current Airman's Information Manual or is operated by a Federal military agency.

(ii) 50 to 1 for a horizontal distance of 10,000 feet from the nearest point of the nearest runway of each airport with its longest runway no more than 3,200 feet in length, excluding heliports, and seaplane bases without specified boundaries, if that airport is either listed in the Airport Directory or is operated by a Federal military agency.

(iii) 25 to 1 for a horizontal distance of 5,000 feet from the nearest point of the nearest landing and take-off area of each heliport listed in the Airport Directory or operated by a Federal military agency.

(3) Any construction or alteration on any airport listed in the Airport Directory of the current Airman's information Manual fi§ 17.7 (c) of this chapter).

(b) A notification to the Federal Aviation Administration is not required for any of the following construction or alteration of Class A station antenna structures.

(1) Any object that would be shielded by existing structures of a permanent and substantial character or by natural terrain or topographic features of equal or greater height, and would be located in the congested area of a city, town, or settlement where it is evident beyond all reasonable doubt that the structure so shielded will not adversely affect safety in air navigation. Applicants claiming such exemption shall submit a statement with their application to the Commission explaining the basis in detail for their finding (§ 17.14 (a) of this chapter).

(2) Any antenna structure of 20 feet or less in height except one that would increase the height of another antenna structure (§ 17.14 (b) of this chapter).

(c) All antennas (both receiving and transmitting) and supporting structures associated or used in conjunction with a Class C or D Citizens Radio Station operated from a fixed location must comply with at least one of the following:

(1) The antenna and its supporting structure does not exceed 20 feet in height above ground level; or

(2) The antenna and its supporting structure does not exceed by more than 20 feet the height of any natural formation, tree or man-made structure on which it is mounted; or

NOTE: A man-made structure is any construction other than a tower, mast, or pole.

(3) The antenna is mounted on the transmitting antenna structure of another authorized radio station and exceeds neither 60 feet above ground level nor the height of the antenna supporting structure of the other station; or

(4) The antenna is mounted on and does not exceed the height of the antenna structure otherwise used solely for receiving purposes, which structue itself complies with subparagraph (1) or (2) of this paragraph.

(5) The antenna is omnidirectional and the highest point of the antenna and its supporting structure does not exceed 60 feet above ground level and the highest point also does not exceed one foot in height above the established airport elevation for each 100 feet of horizontal distance from the nearest point of the nearest airport runway.

NOTE: A work sheet will be made available upon request to assist in determining the maximum permissible height of the antenna structure.

(d) Class C stations operated on frequencies in the 72-76 MHz band shall employ a transmitting antenna which complies with all of the following:

(1) The gain of the antenna shall not exceed that of a half-wave dipole;

(2) The antenna shall be immediately attached to, and an integral part of, the transmitter; and

(3) Only vertical polarization shall be used.

(e) Further details as to whether an

aeronautical study and/or obstruction marking and lighting may be required, and specifications for obstruction marking and lighting when required, may be obtained from Part 17 of this chapter, "Construction, Marking, and Lighting of Antenna Structures."

(f) Subpart I of Part 1 of this chapter contains procedures implementing the National Environmental Policy Act of 1969. Applications for authorization of the construction of certain classes of communications facilities defined as "major actions" in § 1.305 thereof, are required to be accompanied by specified statemtnts. Generally these classes are:

(1) Antenna towers or supporting structures which exceed 300 feet in height and are not located in areas devoted to heavy indsutry or to agriculture.

(2) Communications facilities to be located in the following areas:

(i) Facilities which are to be located in an officially designated wilderness area or in an area whose designation as a wilderness is pending consideration;

(ii) Facilities which are to be located in an officially designated wildlife preserve or in an area whose designation as a wildlife preserve is pending consideration;

(iii) Facilities which will affect districts, sites, buildings, structures or objects, significant in American history, architecture, archaeology or culture, which are listed in the National Register of Historic Places or are eligible for listing (see 36 CFR 800.2 (d) and (f) and 800.10) and

(iv) Facilities to be located in areas which are recognized either nationally or locally for their special scenic or recreational value.

(3) Facilities whose construction will involve extensive change in surface features (e.g. wetland fill, de-forestation or water diversion).

NOTE: The provisions of this paragraph do not include the moutning of FM, television or other antennas comparable thereto in size on an existing building or antenna tower. The use of existing routes, buildings and towers is an environmentally desirable alternative to the construction of new routes or towers and is encouraged.

If the required statements do not accompany the application, the pertinent facts may be brought to the attention of the Commission by any interested person during the course of the license term and considered de novo by the Commission.

SUBPART C—

TECHNICAL REGULATIONS

§ 95.41 Frequencies available.

(a) Frequencies available for assignment to Class A stations:

(1) The following frequencies or frequency pairs are available primarily for assignment to base and mobile stations. They may also be assigned to fixed stations as follows:

(1) Fixed stations which are used to control base stations of a system may be assigned the frequency assigned to the mobile units associated with the base station. Such fixed stations shall comply with the following requirements if they are located within 75 miles of the center of urbanized areas of 200,000 or more population.

(a) If the station is used to control one or more base stations located within 45 degrees of azimuth, a directional antenna having a front-to-back ratio of at least 15 dB shall be used at the fixed station. For other situations where such a directional antenna cannot be used, a cardioid, bidirectional or omnidirectional antenna may be employed. Consistent with reasonable design, the antenna used must, in ecah case, produce a radiation pattern that provides only the coverage necessary to permit satisfactory control of each base station and limit radiation in other directions to the extent feasible.

(b) The strength of the signal of a fixed station controlling a single base station may not exceed the signal strength produced at the antenna terminal of the base receiver by a unit of the associated mobile station, by more than 6 dB. When the station controls more than one base station, the 6 dB control-to-mobile signal difference need be verified at only one of the base station sites. The measurement of the signal strength of the mobile unit must be made when such unit is transmitting from the control station location or, if that is not practical, from a location within one-fourth mile of the control station site.

(c) Each application for a control station to be authorized under the provisions of this paragraph shall be accompanied by a statement certifying that the output power of the proposed station transmitter will be adjusted to comply with the foregoing signal level limitation. Records of the measurements used to determine the signal ratio shall be kept with the station records and shall be made available for inspection by Commission personnel upon request.

(d) Urbanized areas of 200,000 or more population are defined in the U.S. Census of Population, 1960, Vol. 1, table 23, page 50. The centers of urbanized areas are determined from the Appendix, page 226 of the U.S. Commerce publication "Air Line Distance Between Cities in the United States."

(ii) Fixed stations, other than those used to control base stations, which are located 75 or more miles from the center of an urbanized area of 200,000 or more population. The centers of urbanized areas of 200,000 or more population are listed on page 226 of the Appendix to the U.S. Department of Commerce publication "Air Line Distance Between Cities in the United States." When the fixed station is located 100 miles or less from the center of such an urbanized area, the power output may not exceed 15 watts. All fixed systems are limited to a maximum of two frequencies and must employ directional antennas with a front-to-back ratio of at least 15 dB. For two-frequency systems, separation between transmit-receive frequencies is 5 MHz.

Base and Mobile (MHz)	Mobile Only (MHz)
462.550	467.550
462.575	467.575
462.600	467.600
462.625	467.625
462.650	467.650
462.675	467.675
462.700	467.700
462.725	467.725

(2) Conditions governing the operation of stations authorized prior to March 18, 1968:

(i) all base and mobile stations authorized to operate on frequencies other than those listed in subparagraph (1) of this paragraph may continue to operate on those frequencies only until January 1, 1970.

(ii) Fixed stations located 100 or more miles from the center of any urbanized area of 200,000 or more population authorized to operate on frequencies other than those listed in subparagraph (1) of this paragraph will not have to change frequencies provided no interference is caused to the operation of stations in the land mobile service.

(iii) Fixed stations, other than those used to control base stations, located less than 100 miles (75 miles if the transmitter power output does not exceed 15 watts) from the center of any urbanized area of 200,000 or more population must discontinue operation by November 1, 1971. However, any operation after January 1, 1970, must be on frequencies listed in subparagraph (1) of this paragraph.

(iv) Fixed stations, located less than 100 miles from the center of any urbanized area of 200,000 or more population, which are used to control base stations and are authorized to operate

on frequencies other than those listed in subparagraph (1) of this paragraph may continue to operate on those frequencies only until January 1, 1970.

(v) All fixed stations must comply with the applicable technical requirements of subparagraph (1) relating to antennas and radiated signal strength of this paragraph by November 1, 1971.

(vi) Notwithstanding the provisions of subdivisions (i) through (v) of this subparagraph, all stations authorized to operate on frequencies between 465.000 and 465.500 MHz and located within 75 miles of the center of the 20 largest urbanized areas of the United States, may continue to operate on these frequencies only until January 1, 1969. An extension to continue operation on such frequencies until January 1, 1970, may be granted to such station licensees on a case by case basis of the Commission finds that continued operation would not be inconsistent with planned usage of the particular frequency for police purposes. The 20 largest ubranized areas can be found in the U.S. Census of Population, 1960, vol. 1, table 23, page 50. The centers of urbanized areas are determined from the appendix, page 226, of the U.S. Commerce publication, 'Air Line Distance Between Cities in the United States."

(b) [Reserved].

(c) Class C mobile stations may employ only amplitude tone modulation or on-off keying of the unmodulated carrier, on a shared basis with other stations in the Citizens Radio Service on the frequencies and under the conditions specified in the following tables:

(1) For the control of remote objects or devices by radio, or for the remote actuation of devices which are used solely as a means of attracting attention and subject to no protection from interference due to the operation of industrial, scientific, or medical devices

within the 26.96–27.28 MHz band, the following frequencies are available:

(MHz)	(MHz)	MHz
26.995	27.095	27.195
27.045	27.145	¹27.255

¹The frequency 27.255 MHz also is shared with stations in other services.

(2) Subject to the conditions that interference will not be caused to the remote control of industrial equipment operating on the same or adjacent frequencies and to the reception of television transmissions on Channels 4 or 5; and that no protection will be afforded from interference due to the operation of fixed and mobile stations in other services assigned to the same or adjacent frequencies in the band, the following frequencies are available solely for the radio remote control of models used for hobby purposes:

(i) For the radio remote control of any model used used for hoppy purposes:

MHz	MHz	MHz
72.16	72.32	72.96

(ii) For the radio remote control of aircraft models only:

MHz	MHz	MHz
72.08	72.24	72.40
75.64		

(d) The frequencies listed in the following tables are available for use by Class D mobile stations employing radiotelephony only, on a shared basis with other stations in the Citizens Radio Service, and subject to no protection from interference due to the operation of industrial, scientific, or medical devices within the 26.96–27.28 MHz band.

(1) The following frequencies, commonly known as channels, may be used for communication between units of the same station (intrastation) or different stations (intersat)interstation):

MHz	Channel	MHz	Channel
26.965	1	27.125	14
26.975	2	27.135	15
26.985	3	27.155	16
27.005	4	27.165	17
27.015	5	27.175	18
27.025	6	27.185	19
27.035	7	27.205	20
27.055	8	27.215	21
27.075	10	27.225	22
27.105	12	27.55	23
27.115	13		

(2) The frequency 27.065 MHz (Channel 9) shall be used solely for:

(i) Emergency communications involving the immediate safety of life of individuals or the immediate protection of property or

(ii) Communications necessary to render assistance to a motorist.

NOTE: A licensee, before using Channel 9, must make a determination that his communication is either or both (a) an emergency communication or (b) is necessary to render assistance to a motorist. To be an emergency communication, the message must have some direct relation to the immediate safety of life or immediate protection of property. If no immediate action is required, it is not an emergency. What may not be an emergency under one set of circumstances may be an emergency under different circumstances. There are many worthwhile public service communications that do not qualify as emergency communications. In the case of motorist assistance, the message must be necessary to assist a particular motorist and not, except in a valid emergency, motorists in general. If the communications are to be lengthy, the exchange should be shifted to another channel, if feasible, after contact is established. No nonemergency or nonmotorist assistance communications are permitted on Channel 9 even for the limited purpose of calling a licensee monitoring a channel to ask him to switch to another channel. Although Channel 9 may be used for marine emergencies, it should not be considered a substitute for the authorized marine distress system. The Coast Guard has stated it will not "participate directly in the Citizens Radio Service by fitting with and/or providing a watch on any Citizens Band Channel. (Coast Guard Commandant Instruction 2302.6)"

The following are examples of permitted and prohibited types of communications. They are guidelines and are not intended to be all inclusive.

Permitted   Example   message
Yes.... "A tornado sighted six miles north of town."
No..... "This is observation post number 10. No tornados sighted."
Yes.... "I am out of gas on Interstate 95."
No..... "I am out of gas in my driveway."
Yes.... "There is a four-car collision at Exit 10 on the Beltway, send police and ambulance."
No..... "Traffic is moving smoothly on the Beltway."
Yes.... "Base to Unit 1, the Weather bureau has just issued a thunderstorm warning. Bring the sailboat into port."
No..... "Attention all motorists. The Weather Bureau advises that the snow tomorrow will accumulate 4 to 6 inches."
Yes.... "There is a fire in the building on the corner of 6th and Main Streets."
No..... "This is Haloween patrol unit number 3. Everything is quiet here."

The following priorities should be observed in the use of Channel 9.

1. Communications relating to an existing situation dangerous to life or property, i.e., fire, automobile accident.

2. Communications relating to a potentially hazardous situation, i.e., car stalled in a dangerous place, lost child, boat out of gas.

3. Road assistance to a disabled vehicle on the highway or street.

4. Road and street directions.

(3) The frequency 27.085 MHz (Channel 11) shall be used only as a calling frequency for the sole purpose of establishing communications and moving to another frequency (channel) to conduct communications.

(e) Upon specific request accompanying application for renewal of station authorization, a Class A station in this service, which was authorized to operate on a frequency in the 460–461 MHz band until March 31, 1967, may be assigned that frequency for continued use until not later than March 31, 1968, subject to all other provisions of this part.

§ 95.43 Transmitter power.

(a) Transmitter power is the power at the transmitter output terminals and delivered to the antenna, antenna transmission line, or any other impedance-matched, radio frequency load.

(1) For single sideband transmitters and other transmitters employing a reduced carrier, a suppressed carrier or a controlled carrier, used at Class D stations, transmitter power is the peak envelope power.

(2) For all transmitters other than those covered by paragraph (a) (1) of this section, the transmitter power is the carrier power.

(b) The transmitter power of a station shall not exceed the following values under any condition of modulation or other circumstances.

Class of station:	Transmitter power in watts
A	50
C—27.255 MHz	25
C—26.995–27.195 MHz	4
C—72–76 MHz	0.75
D—Carrier (where applicable)	4
D—Peak envelope power (where applicable)	12

§ 95.44 External radio frequency power amplifiers prohibited.

No external radio frequency power amplifier shall be used or attached, by connection, coupling attachment or in any other way at any Class D station.

NOTE: An external radio frequency power amplifier at a Class D station will be presumed to have been used where it is in the operator's possession or on his premisis and there is extrinsic evidence of any operation of such Class D station in excess of power limitations provided under this rule part unless the operator of such equipment holds a station license in another radio service under which license the use of the said amplifier at its maximum rated output power is permitted.

§ 95.45 Frequency tolerance.

(a) Except as provided in paragraphs (b) and (c) of this section, the carrier frequency of a transmitter in this service shall be maintained within the following percentage of the authorized frequency:

Class of station	Frequency tolerance	
	Fixed and base	Mobile
A	0.00025	0.0005
C		.005
D		.005

(b) Transmitters used at Class C stations operating on authorized frequencies between 26.99 and 27.26 MHz with 2.5 watts or less mean output power, which are used solely for the control of remote objects or devices by radio (other than devices used solely as a means of attracting attention), are permitted a frequency tolerance of 0.01 percent.

(c) Class A stations operated at a fixed location used to control base stations, through use of a mobile only frequency, may operate with a frequency tolerance of 0.0005 percent.

§ 95.47 Types of emission.

(a) Except as provided in paragraph (e) of this section, Class A stations in this service will normally be authorized to transmit radiotelephony only. However, the use of tone signals or signaling devices solely to actuate receiver circuits, such as tone operated squelch or selective calling circuits, the primary function of which is to establish or establish and maintain voice communications, is permitted. The use of tone signals solely to attract attention is prophibited.

(b) [Reserved].

(c) Class C stations in this service are authorized to use amplitude tone modulation or on-off unmodulated carrier only, for the control of remote objects or devices by radio or for the remote actuation of devices which are used solely as a means of attracting attention. The transmission of any form of telegraphy, telephony or record communications by a Class C station is prohibited. Telemetering, except for the transmission of simple, short duration signals indicating the presence or absence of a condition or the occurrence of an event, is also prohibited.

(d) Transmitters used in Class D stations in this service are authorized to use amplitude voice modulation, either single or double sideband. Tone signals or signalling devices may be used only to actuate receiver circuits, such as tone operated squelch or selective calling circuits, the primary function of which is to establish or maintain voice communications. The use of any signals solely to attract attention or for the control of remote objects or devices is prohibited.

(e) Other types of emission not described in paragraph (a) of this section may be authorized for Class A citizens radio stations upon a showing of need therefore. An application requesting such authorization shall fully describe the emission desired, shall indicate the bandwidth required for satisfactory communication, and shall state the purpose for which such emission is required. For information regarding the classification of emissions and the calculation of bandwidth, reference should be made to Part 2 of this chapter.

§ 95.49 Emission limitations.

(a) Each authorization issued to a Class A citizens radio station will show, as a prefix to the classification of the authorized emission, a figure specifying the maximum bandwidth to be occupied by the emission.

(b) [Reserved]

(c) The authorized bandwidth of the emission of any transmitter employing amplitude modulation shall be 8 kHz for double sideband, 4 kHz for single sideband and the authorized bandwidth of the emission of transmitters employing frequency or phase modulation (Class F2 or F3) shall be 20 kHz. The use of class F2 and F3 emissions in the frequency band 26.96–27.28 MHz is not authorized.

(d) The mean power of emissions shall be attenuated below the mean power of the transmitter in accordance with the following schedule:

(1) When using emissions other than single sideband:

(i) On any frequency removed from the center of the authorized bandwidth by more than 50 percent up to and including 100 percent of the authorized bandwidth: at least 25 decibels;

(ii) On any frequency removed from the center of the authorized bandwidth by more than 100 percent up to and including 250 percent of the authorized bandwidth: At least 35 decibels;

(2) When using single sideband emissions:

(i) On any frequency removed from the center of the authorized bandwidth by more than 50 percent up to and including 150 percent of the authorized bandwidth: At least 25 decibels;

(3) On any frequency removed from the center of the authorized bandwidth by more than 250 percent of the authorized bandwidth: At least 43 plus 10 $\log_{10}$ (mean power in watts) decibels.

(e) When an unauthorized emission results in harmful interference, the Commission may, in its discretion, require appropriate technical changes in equipment to alleviate the interference.

§ 95.51 Modulation requirements.

(a) When double sideband, amplitude modulation is used for telephony, the modulation percentage shall be sufficient to provide efficient communication and shall not exceed 100 percent.

(b) Each transmitter for use in Class D stations, other than single sideband, suppressed carrier, or controlled carrier, for which type acceptance is requested after May 24, 1974, having more than 2.5 watts maximum output power shall be equipped with a device which automatically prevents modulation in excess of 100 percent on positive and negative peaks.

(c) The maximum audio frequency required for satisfactory radiotelephone intelligibility for use in this service is considered to be 3000 Hz.

(d) Transmitters for use at Class A stations shall be provided with a device which automatically will prevent greater than normal audio level from causing modulation in excess of that specified in this subpart; *Provided, however,* That the requirements of this paragraph shall not apply to transmitters authorized at mobile stations and having an output power of 2.5 watts or less.

(e) Each transmitter of a Class A station which is equipped with a modulation limiter in accordance with the provisions of paragraph (d) of this section shall also be equipped with an audio low-pass filter. This audio low-pass filter shall be installed between the modulation limiter and the modulated stage and, at audio frequencies between 3 kHz and 20 kHz, shall have an attenuation greater than the attenuation at 1 kHz by at least:

$$60 \log_{10} (f/3) \text{ decibels}$$

where "f" is the audio frequency in kHz. At audio frequencies above 20 kHz, the attenuation shall be at least 50 decibels greater than the attenuation at 1 kHz.

(f) Simultaneous amplitude modulation and frequency or phase modulation of a transmitter is not authorized.

(g) The maximum frequency deviation of frequency modulated transmitters used at Class A stations shall not exceed 5 k Hz.

§ 95.53 Compliance with technical requirements.

(a) Upon receipt of notification from the Commission of a deviation from the technical requirements of the rules in this part, the radiations of the transmitter involved shall be suspended immediately, except for necessary tests and adjustments, and shall not be resumed until such deviation has been corrected.

(b) When any citizens radio station licensee receives a notice of violation indicating that the station has been operated contrary to any of the provisions contained in Subpart C of this part, or where it otherwise appears that operation of a station in this service may not be in accordance with applicable technical standards, the Commission may require the licensee to conduct such tests as may be necessary to determine whether the equipment is capable of meeting these standards and to make such adjustments as may be necessary to assure compliance therewith. A licensee who is notified that he is required to conduct such tests and/or make adjustments must, within the time limit specified in the notice, report to the Commission the results thereof.

(c) All tests and adjustments which may be required in accordance with paragraph (b) of this section shall be made by, or under the immediate supervision of, a person holding a first- or second-class commercial operator license, either radiotelephone or radio telegraph as may be appropriate for the type of emission employed. In each case, the report which is submitted to the Commission shall be signed by the licensed commercial operator. Such report shall describe the results of the tests and adjustments, the test equipment and procedures used, and shall state the type, class, and serial number of the operator's license. A copy of this report shall also be kept with the station records.

§ 95.55 Acceptability of transmitters for licensing.

Transmitters type approved or type accepted for use under this part are included in the Commission's Radio Equipment List. Copies of this list are available for public reference at the Commission's Washington, D.C., offices and field offices. The requirements for transmitters which may be operated under a license in this service are set forth in the following paragraphs.

(a) Class C stations:

(1) Transmitters operated in the band 72–76 MHz shall be type accepted.

(2) All transmitters operated in the band 26.99–27.26 MHz shall be type approved, type accepted or crystal controlled.

(c) Class D Stations:

(1) All transmitters first licensed, or marketed as specified in § 2.805 of this chapter, prior to November 22, 1974, shall be type accepted or crystal controlled.

(2) All transmitters first licensed, or marketed as specified in § 2.803 of this chapter, on or after November 22, 1974, shall be type accepted.

(3) Effective November 23, 1978, all transmitters shall be type accepted.

(4) Transmitters which are equipped to operate on any frequency not included in §95.41(d)(1) may not be installed at, or used by, any Class D station unless there is a station license posted at the transmitter location, or a transmitter identification card (FCC Form 452–C) attached to the transmitter, which indicates that operation of the transmitter on such frequency has been authorized by the Commission.

(d) With the exception of equipment type approved for use at a Class C station, all transmitting equipment authorized in this service shall be crystal controlled.

(e) No controls, switches or other functions which can cause operation in violation of the technical regulations of this part shall be accessible from the operating panel or exterior to the cabinet enclosing a transmitter authorized in this service.

§95.57 Procedure for type acceptance of equipment.

(a) Any manufacturer of a transmitter built for use in this service, except noncrystal controlled transmitters for use at Class C stations, may request type acceptance for such transmitter in accordance with the type acceptance requirements of this part, following the type acceptance procedure set forth in Part 2 of this chapter.

(b) Type acceptance for an individual transmitter may also be requested by an applicant for a station authorization by following the type acceptance procedures set forth in Part 2 of this chapter. Such transmitters, if accepted, will not normally be included on the Commission's "Radio Equipment List", but will be individually enumerated on the station authorization.

(c) Additional rules with respect to type acceptance are set forth in Part 2 of this chapter. These rules include information with respect to withdrawal of type acceptance, modification of type-accepted equipment, and limitations on the findings upon which type acceptance is based.

(d) Transmitters equipped with a frequency or frequencies not listed in §95.41(d)(1) will not be type accepted for use at Class D stations unless the transmitter is also type accepted for use in the service in which the frequency is authorized, if type acceptance in that service is required.

§ 95.58 Additional requirements for type acceptance.

(a) All transmitters shall be crystal controlled.

(b) Except for transmitters type accepted for use at Class A stations, transmitters shall not include any provisions for increasing power to levels in excess of the pertinent limits specified in Section 95.43.

(c) In addition to all other applicable technical requirements set forth in this part, transmitters for which type acceptance is requested after May 24, 1974, for use at Class D stations shall comply with the following:

(1) Single sideband transmitters and other transmitters employing reduced, suppressed or controlled carrier shall include a means for automatically preventing the transmitter power from exceeding either the maximum permissible peak envelope power or the rated peak envelope power of the transmitter, whichever is lower.

(2) Multi-frequency transmitters shall not provide more than 23 transmitting frequencies, and the frequency selector shall be limited to a single control.

(3) Other than the channel selector switch, all transmitting frequency determining circuitry, including crystals, employed in Class D station equipment shall be internal to the equipment and shall not be accessible from the exterior of the equipment cabinet or operating panel.

(4) Single sideband transmitters shall be capable of transmitting on the upper sideband. Capability for transmission also on the lower sideband is permissible.

(5) The total dissipation ratings, established by the manufacturer of the electron tubes or semiconductors which supply radio frequency power to the antenna terminals of the transmitter, shall not exceed 10 watts. For electron tubes, the rating shall be the Intermittent Commercial and Amateur Service (ICAS plate dissipation value if established. For semiconductors, the rating shall be the collector or device dissipation value, whichever is greater, which may be temperature de-rated to not more than 50° C.

(d) Only the following external transmitter controls, connections or devices will normally be permitted in transmitters for which type acceptance is requested after May 24, 1974, for use at Class D stations. Approval of additional controls, connections or devices may be given after consideration of the function to be performed by such additions.

(1) Primary power connection. (Circuitry or devices such as rectifiers, transformers, or inverters which provide the nominal rated transmitter primary supply voltage may be used without voiding the transmitter type acceptance.)

(2) Microphone connection.

(3) Radio frequency output power connection.

(4) Audio frequency power amplifier output connector and selector switch.

(5) On-off switch for primary power to transmitter. May be combined with receiver controls such as the receiver on-off switch and volume control.

(6) Upper-lower sideband selector; for single sideband transmitters only.

(7) Selector for choice of carrier level; for single sideband transmitters only. May be combined with sideband selector.

(8) Transmitting frequency selector switch.

(9) Transmit-receive switch.

(10) Meter(s) and selector switch for monitoring transmitter performance.

(11) Pilot lamp or meter to indicate the presence of radio frequency output power or that transmitter control circuits are activated to transmit.

(e) An instruction book for the user shall be furnished with each transmitter sold and one copy (a draft or preliminary copy is acceptable providing a final copy is furnished when completed) shall be forwarded to the Commission with each request for type acceptance or type approval. The book shall contain all information necessary for the proper installation and operation of the transmitter including:

(1) Instructions concerning all controls, adjustments and switches which may be operated or adjusted without causing violation of technical regulations of this part;

(2) Warnings concerning any adjustment which, according to the rules of this part, may be made only by, or under the immediate supervision of, a person holding a commercial first or second class radio operator license;

(3) Warnings concerning the replacement or substitution of crystals, tubes or other components which could cause violation of the technical regulations of this part and of the type acceptance or type approval requirements of Part 2 of this chapter.

(4) Warnings concerning licensing requirements and details concerning the application procedures for licensing.

§95.59 Submission of noncrystal controlled Class C station transmitters for type approval.

Type approval of noncrystal controlled transmitters for use at Class C stations in this service may be requested in accordance with the procedure specified in Part 2 of this chapter.

§95.61 Type approval of receiver-transmitter combinations.

Type approval will not be issued for transmitting equipment for operation under this part when such equipment is enclosed in the same cabinet, is constructed on the same chassis in whole or in part, or is identified with a common type or model number with a radio receiver, unless such receiver has been certificated to the Commission as complying with the requirements of Part 15 of this chapter.

§95.63 Minimum equipment specifications.

Transmitters submitted for type approval in this service shall be capable of meeting the technical specifications contained in this part, and in addition, shall comply with the following:

(a) Any basic instructions concerning the proper adjustment, use, or operation of the equipment that may be necessary shall be attached to the equipment in a suitable manner and in such positions as to be easily read by the operator.

(b) A durable nameplate shall be mounted on each transmitter showing the name of the manufacturer, the type or model designation, and providing suitable space for permanently displaying the transmitter serial number, FCC type approval number, and the class of station for which approved.

(c) The transmitter shall be designed, constructed, and adjusted by the manufacturer to operate on a frequency or frequencies available to the class of station for which type approval is sought. In designing the equipment, every reasonable precaution shall be taken to protect the user from high voltage shock and radio frequency burns. Connections to batteries (if used) shall be made in such a manner as to permit replacement by the user without causing improper operation of the transmitter. Generally accepted modern engineering principles shall be utilized in the generation of radio frequency currents so as to guard against unnecessary interference to other services. In cases of harmful interference arising from the design, construction, or operation of the equipment, the Commission may require appropriate technical changes in equipment to alleviate interference.

(d) Controls which may effect changes in the carrier frequency of the transmitter shall not be accessible from the exterior of any unit unless such accessibility is specifically approved by the Commission.

§95.65 Test procedure.

Type approval tests to determine whether radio equipment meets the technical specifications contained in this part will be conducted under the following conditions:

(a) Gradual ambient temperature variations from 0° to 125° F.

(b) Relative ambient humidity from 20 to 95 percent. This test will normally consist of subjecting the equipment for at least three consecutive periods of 24 hours each, to a relative ambient humidity of 20, 60, and 95 percent, respectively, at a temperature of approximately 80° F.

(c) Movement of transmitter or objects in the immediate vicinity thereof.

(d) Power supply voltage variations normally to be encountered under actual operating conditions.

(e) Additional tests as may be prescribed, if considered necessary or desirable.

§ 95.67 Certificate of type approval.

A certificate or notice of type approval, when issued to the manufacturer of equipment intended to be used or operated in the Citizens Radio Service, constitutes a recognition that on the basis of the test made, the particular type of equipment appears to have the capability of functioning in accordance with the technical specifications and regulations contained in this part: *Provided,* That all such additional equipment of the same type is properly constructed, maintained, and operated: *And provided further,* That no change whatsoever is made in the design or construction of such equipment except upon specific approval by the Commission.

SUBPART D

STATION OPERATING REQUIREMENTS

§95.81 Permissible communications

Stations licensed in the Citizens Radio Service are authorized to transmit the following types of communications:

(a) Communications to facilitate the personal or business activities of the licensee.

(b) Communication relating to:

(1) the immediate safety of life or the immediate protection of property in accordance with §95.85.

(2) the rendering of assistance to a motorist, mariner or other traveler.

(3) civil defense activities in accordance with §95.87.

(4) other activities only as specifically authorized pursuant to §95.87.

(c) Communications with stations authorized in other radio services except as prohibited in §95.83 (a) (3).

§95.83 Prohibited communications.

(a) A citizens radio station shall not be used:

(1) For any purpose, or in connection with any activity, which is contrary to Federal, State, or local law.

(2) For the transmission of communications containing obscene, indecent, profane words, language, or meaning.

(3) To communicate with an Amateur Radio Service station, an unlicensed station, or foreign stations (other than as provided in Subpart E of this part) except for communications pursuant to §§95.85 (b) and 95.121.

(4) To convey program material for retransmission, live or delayed, on a broadcast facility.

NOTE: A Class A or Class D station may be used in connection with the administrative, engineering, or maintenance activities of a broadcasting station; a Class A or Class C station may be used for control functions by radio which do not involve the transmission of program material; and a Class A or Class D station may be used in the gathering of news items or preparation of programs: *Provided*, That the actual or recorded transmissions of the Citizens radio station are not broadcast at any time in whole or in part.

(5) To intentionally interfere with the communications of another station.

(6) For the direct transmission of any material to the public through a public address system or similar means.

(7) For the transmission of music, whistling, sound effects, or any material for amusement or entertainment purposes, or solely to attract attention.

(8) To transmit the word "MAYDAY" or other international distress signals, except when the station is located in a ship, aircraft, or other vehicle which is threatened by grave and imminent danger and requests immediate assistance.

(9) For advertising or soliciting the sale of any goods or services.

(10) For transmitting messages in other than plain language. Abbreviations including nationally or internationally recognized operating signals, may be used only if a list of all such abbreviations and their meaning is kept in the station records and made available to any Commission representative on demand.

(11) To carry on communications for hire, whether the renumeration or benefit received is direct or indirect.

(b) A Class D station may not be used to communicate with, or attempt to communicate with, any unit of the same or another station over a distance of more than 150 miles.

(c) A licensee of a Citizens radio station who is engaged in the business of selling Citizens radio transmitting equipment shall not allow a customer to operate under his station license. In addition, all communications by the licensee for the purpose of demonstrating such equipment shall consist only of brief messages addressed to other units of the same station.

§95.85 Emergency and assistance to motorist use.

(a) All Citizens radio stations shall give priority to the emergency communications of other stations which involve the immediate safety of life of individuals or the immediate protection of property.

(b) Any station in this service may be utilized during an emergency involving the immediate safety of life of individuals or the immediate protection of property for the transmission of emergency communications. It may also be used to transmit communications necessary to render assistance to a motorist.

(1) When used for transmission of emergency communications certain provisions in this part concerning use of frequencies (§95.41 (d)); prohibited uses (§95.83 (a) (3); operation by or on behalf of persons other than the licensee (§95.91 (a) and (b)) shall not apply.

(2) When used for transmission of communications necessary to render assistance to a traveler, the provisions of this Part concerning duration of transmission (§95.91 (b)) shall not apply.

(3) The exemptions granted from certain rule provisions in subparagraphs (1) and (2) of this paragraph may be rescinded by the Commission at its discretion.

(c) If the emergency use under paragraph (b) of this section extends over a period of 12 hours or more, notice shall be sent to the Commission in Washington, D.C., as soon as it is evident that the emergency has or will exceed 12

hours. The notice should include the identity of the stations participating, the nature of the emergency, and the use made of the stations. A single notice covering all participating stations may be submitted.

§95.87 Operation by, or on behalf of, persons other than the licensee.

(a) Transmitters authorized in this service must be under the control of the licensee at all times. A licensee whall not transfer, assign, or dispose of, in any manner, directly or indirectly, the operating authority under his station license, and shall be responsible for the proper operation of all units of the station.

(b) Citizens radio stations may be operated only by the following persons, except as provided in paragraph (c) of this section:

(1) The licensee;

(2) Members of the licensee's immediate family living in the same household;

(3) The partners, if the licensee is a partnership, provided the communications relate to the business of the partnership;

(4) The members, if the licensee is an unincorporated association, provided the communications relate to the business of the association;

(5) Employees of the licensee only while acting within the scope of their employment;

(6) Any person under the control or supervision of the licensee when the station is used solely for the control of remote objects or devices, other than devices used only as a means of attracting attention; and

(7) Other persons, upon specific prior approval of the Commission shown on or attached to the station license, under the following circumstances:

(i) Licensee is a corporation and proposes to provide private radiocommunication facilities for the transmission of messages or signals by or on behalf of its parent corporation, another subsidiary of the parent corporation, or its own subsidiary. Any remuneration or compensation received by the licensee for the use of the radiocommunication facilities shall be governed by a contract entered into by the parties concerned and the total of the compensation shall not exceed the cost of providing the facilities. Records which show the cost of service and its nonprofit or cost-sharing basis shall be maintained by the licensee.

(ii) Licensee proposes the shared or cooperative use of a Class A station with one or more other licensees in this service for the purpose of communicating on a regular basis with units of their respective Class A stations, or with units of other Class A stations if the communications transmitted are otherwise permissible. The use of these private radiocommunication facilities shall be conducted pursuant to a written contract which shall provide that contributions to capital and operating expense shall be made on a nonprofit, cost-sharing basis, the cost to be divided on an equitable basis among all parties to the agreement. Records which show the cost of service and its nonprofit, cost-sharing basis shall be maintained by the licensee. In any case, however, licensee must show a separate and independent need for the particular units proposed to be shared to fulfill his own communications requirements.

(iii) Other cases where there is a need for other persons to operate a unit of licensee's radio station. Requests for authority may be made either at the time of the filing of the application for station license or thereafter by letter. In either case, the licensee must show the nature of the proposed use and that it relates to an activity of the licensee, how he proposes to maintain control over the transmitters at all times, and why it is not appropriate for such other person to obtain a station license in his own name. The authority, if granted, may be specific with respect to the names of the persons who are permitted to operate, or may authorize operation by unnamed persons for specific purposes. This authority may be revoked by the Commission, in its discretion, at any time.

(c) An individual who was formerly a citizens radio station licensee shall not be permitted to operate any citizens radio station of the same class licensed to another person until such time as he again has been issued a valid radio station license of that class, when his license has been:

(1) Revoked by the Commission.

(2) Surrendered for cancellation after the institution of revocation proceedings by the Commission.

(3) Surrendered for cancellation after a notice of apparent liability to forfeiture has been served by the Commission.

§95.89 Telephone answering services.

(a) Notwithstanding the provisions of §95.87, a licensee may install a transmitting unit of his station on the premises of a telephone answering service. The same unit may not be operated under the authorization of more than one licensee. In all cases, the licensee must enter into a written agreement with the answering service. This agreement must be kept with the licensee's station records and must provide, as a minimum, that:

(1) The licensee will have control over the operation of the radio unit at all times;

(2) The licensee will have full and unrestricted access to the transmitter to enable him to carry out his responsibilities under his license;

(3) Both parties understand that the licensee is fully responsible for the pro-

per operation of the citizens radio station; and

(4) The unit so furnished shall be used only for the transmission of communications to other units belonging to the licensee's station.

(b) A citizens radio station licensed to a telephone answering service shall not be used to relay messages or transmit signals to its customers.

§95.91 Duration of transmissions.

(a) All communications or signals, regardless of their nature, shall be restricted to the minimum practicable transmission time. The radiation of energy shall be limited to transmissions modulated or keyed for actual permissible communications, tests, or control signals. Continuous or uninterrupted transmissions from a single station or between a number of communicating stations is prohibited, except for communications involving the immediate safety of life or property.

(b) All communications between Class D stations (interstation) shall be restricted to not longer than five continuous minutes. At the conclusion of this 5 minute period, or the exchange of less than 5 minutes, the participating stations shall remain silent for at least one minute.

(c) All communication between units of the same Class D Station (intrastation) shall be restricted to the minimum practicable transmission.

(d) The transmission of audible tone signals or a sequence of tone signals for the operation of the tone operated squelch or selective calling circuits in accordance with §95.47 shall not exceed a total of 15 seconds duration. Continuous transmission of a subaudible tone for this purpose is permitted. For the purposes of this section, any tone or combination of tones having no frequency above 150 hertz shall be considered subaudible.

(e) The transmission of permissible control signals shall be limited to the minimum practicable time necessary to accomplish the desired control or actuation of remote objects or devices. The continuous radiation of energy for periods exceeding 3 minutes duration for the purpose of transmission of control signals shall be limited to control functions requiring at least one or more changes during each minute of such transmission. However, while it is actually being used to control model aircraft in flight by means of interrupted tone modulation of its carrier, a citizens radio station may transmit a continuous carrier without being simultaneously modulated if the presence or absence of the carrier also performs a control function. An exception to the limitations contained in this paragraph may be authorized upon a satisfactory showing that a continuous control signal is required to perform a control function which is necessary to insure the safety of life or property.

§95.93 Tests and adjustments.

All tests or adjustments of citizens radio transmitting equipment involving an external connection to the radio frequency output circuit shall be made using a nonradiating dummy antenna. However, a brief test signal, either with or without modulation, as appropriate, amy be transmitted when it is necessary to adjust a transmitter to an antenna for a new station installation or for an existing installation involving a change of antenna or change of transmitters, or when necessary for the detection, measurement, and suppression of harmonic or other spurious radiation. Test transmissions using a radiating antenna shall not exceed a total of 1 minute during any 5-minute period, shall not interfere with communications already in progress on the operating frequency, and shall be properly identified as required by §95.95, but may otherwise be unmodulated as appropriate.

§95.95 Station identification.

(a) The call sign of a citizens radio station shall consist of three letters followed by four digits.

(b) Each transmission of the station call sign shall be made in the English language by each unit, shall be complete, and each letter and digit shall be separately and distinctly transmitted. Only standard phonetic alphabets, nationally or internationally recognized, may be used in lieu of pronunciation of letters for voice transmission of call signs. A unit designator or special identification may be used in addition to the station call sign but not as a substitute therefor.

(c) Except as provided in paragraph (d) of this section, all transmission from each unit of a citizens radio station shall be identified by the transmission of its assigned call sign at the beginning and end of each transmission or series of transmissions, but at least at intervals not to exceed ten (10) minutes.

(d) Unless specifically required by the station authorization, the transmissions of a citizens radio station need not be identified when the station (1) is a Class A station which automatically retransmits the information received by radio from another station which is properly identified or (2) is not being used for telephony emission.

(e) In lieu of complying with the requirements of paragraph (c) of this section, Class A base stations, fixed stations, and mobile units when communicating with base stations may identify as follows:

(1) Base stations and fixed stations of a Class A radio system shall transmit their call signs at the end of each transmission or exchange of transmissions, or once each 15-minute period of a continuous exchange of communications.

(2) A mobile unit of a Class A station communicating with a base station of a Class A radio system on the same frequency shall transmit once during each exchange of transmissions any unit identifier which is on file in the station records of such base station.

(3) A mobile unit of Class A stations communicating with a base station of a Class A radio system on a different frequency shall transmit its call sign at the end of each transmission or exchange of transmissions, or once each 15-minute period of a continuous exchange of communications.

§95.97 Operator license requirements.

(a) No operator license is required for the operation of a citizens radio station except that stations manually transmitting Morse Code shall be operated by the holders of a third or higher class radiotelegraph operator license.

(b) Except as provided in paragraph (c) of this section, all transmitter adjustments or tests while radiating energy during or coincident with the construction, installation, servicing, or maintenance of a radio station in this service, which may affect the proper operation of such stations, shall be made by or under the immediate supervision and responsibility of a person holding a first- or second-class commercial radio operator license, either radiotelephone or radio telegraph, as may be appropriate for the type of emission employed, and such person shall be responsible for the proper functioning of the station equipment at the conclusion of such adjustments or tests. Further, in any case where a transmitter adjustment which may affect the proper operation of the transmitter has been made while not radiating energy by a person not the holder of the required commercial radio operator license or not under the supervision of such licensed operator, other than the factory assembling or repair of equipment, the transmitter shall be checked for compliance with the technical requirements of the rules by a commercial radio operator of the proper grade before it is placed on the air.

(c) Except as provided in §95.53 and in paragraph (d) of this section, no commercial radio operator license is required to be held by the person performing transmitter adjustments or tests during or coincident with the construction, installation, servicing, or maintenance of Class C transmitters, or Class D transmitters used at stations authorized prior to May 24, 1974: *Provided*, That there is compliance with all of the following conditions ;

(1) The transmitting equipment shall be crystal-controlled with a crystal capable of maintaining the station frequency within the prescribed tolerance;

(2) The transmitting equipment either shall have been factory assembled or shall have been provided in kit form by a manufacturer who provided all components together with full and detailed instructions for their assembly by nonfactory personnel;

(3) The frequency determining elements of the transmitter, including the crystal(s) and all other components of the crystal oscillator circuit, shall have been preassembled by the manufacturer, pretuned to a specific available frequency, and sealed by the manufacturer so that replacement of any component or any adjustment which might cause off-frequency operation cannot be made without breaking such seal and thereby voiding the certification of the manufacturer required by this paragraph;

(4) The transmitting equipment shall have been so designed that none of the transmitter adjustments or tests normally performed during or coincident with the installation, servicing, or maintenance of the station, or during

the normal rendition of the service of the station, or during the final assembly of kits or partially preassembled units, may reasonably be expected to result in off-frequency operation, excessive input power, overmodulation, or excessive harmonics or other spurious emissions; and

(5) The manufacturer of the transmitting equipment or of the kit from which the transmitting equipment is assembled shall have certified in writing to the purchaser of the equipment and to the Commission

§95.101 Posting station license and transmitter identification cards or plates.

(a) The current authorization, or a clearly legible photocopy thereof, for each station (including units of a Class C or Class D station) operated at a fixed location shall be posted at a conspicuous place at the principal fixed location from which such station is controlled, and a photocopy of such authorization shall also be posted at all other fixed locations from which the station is controlled. If a photocopy of the authorization is posted at the principal control point, the location of the original shall be stated on that photocopy. In addition, an executed Transmitter Identification Card (FCC Form 452–C) or a plate of metal or other durable substance, legibly indicating the call sign and the licensee's name and address, shall be affixed, readily visible for inspection, to each transmitter operated at a fixed location when such transmitter is not in view of, or is not readily accessible to, the operator of at least one of the locations at which the station authorization or a photocopy thereof is required to be posted.

(b) The current authorization for each station operated as a mobile station shall be retained as a permanent part of the station records, but need not be posted. In addition, an executed Transmitter Identification Card (FCC Form 452–C) or a plate of metal or other durable substance, legibly indicating the call sign and the licensee's name and address, shall be affixed, readily visible for inspection, to each of such transmitters: *Provided*, That, if the transmitter is not in view of the location from which it is controlled, or is not readily accessible for inspection, then such card or plate shall be affixed to the control equipment at the transmitter operating position or posted adjacent thereto.

§95.103 Inspection of stations and station records.

All stations and records of stations in the Citizens Radio Service shall be made available for inspection upon the request of an authorized representative of the Commission made to the licensee or to his representative (see §1.6 of this chapter). Unless otherwise stated in this part, all required station records shall be maintained for a period of at least 1 year.

§95.105 Current copy of rules required.

Each licensee in this service shall maintain as a part of his station records a current copy of Part 95, Citizens Radio Service, of this chapter.

§95.107 Inspection and maintenance of tower marking and lighting, and associated control equipment.

The licensee of any radio station which has an antenna structure required to be painted and illuminated pursuant to the provisions of section 303(q) of the Communications Act of 1934, as amended, and Part 17 of this chapter, shall perform the inspection and maintain the tower marking and lighting, and associated control equipment, in accordance with the requirements set forth in Part 17 of this chapter.

§95.111 Recording of tower light inspections.

When a station in this service has an antenna structure which is required to be illuminated, appropriate entries shall be made in the station records in conformity with the requirements set forth in Part 17 of this chapter.

§95.113 Answer to notices of violations.

(a) Any licensee who appears to have violated any provision of the Communications Act or any provision of this chapter shall be served with a written notice calling the facts to his attention and requesting a statement concerning the matter. FCC Form 793 may be used for this purpose.

(b) Within 10 days from receipt of notice or such other period as may be specified, the licensee shall send a written answer, in duplicate, direct to the office of the Commission originating the notice. If an answer cannot be sent nor an acknowledgment made within such period by reason of illness or other unavoidable circumstances, acknowledgment and answer shall be made at the earliest practicable date with a satisfactory explanation of the delay.

(c) The answer to each notice shall be complete in itself and shall not be abbreviated by reference to other communications or answers to other notices. In every instance the answer shall contain a statement of the action taken to correct the condition or omission complained of and to preclude its recurrence. If the notice relates to violations that may be due to the physical or electrical characteristics of transmitting apparatus, the licensee must comply with the provisions of §95.53, and the answer to the notice shall state fully what steps, if any, have been taken to prevent future violations, and, if any new apparatus is to be installed, the date such apparatus was ordered, the name of the manufacturer, and the promised date of delivery. If the installation of such apparatus requires a construction permit, the file number of the application shall be given, or if a file number has not been assigned by the Commission, such identification shall be given as will permit ready identification of the application. If the notice of violation relates to lack of attention to or improper operation of the transmitter, the name and license number of the operator in charge, if any, shall also be given.

§95.115 False signals.

No person shall transmit false or deceptive communications by radio or identify the station he is operating by means of a call sign which has not been assigned to that station.

§95.117 Station location.

(a) The specific location of each Class A base station and each Class A fixed station and the specific area of operation of each Class A mobile station shall be indicated in the application for license. An authorization may be granted for the operation of a Class A base station or fixed station in this service at unspecified temporary fixed locations within a specified general area of operation. However, when any unit or units of a base station or fixed station authorized to be operated at temporary locations actually remains or is intended to remain at the same location for a period of over a year, application for separate authorization specifying the fixed location shall be made as soon as possible but not later than 30 days after the expiration of the 1-year period.

(b) A Class A mobile station authorized in this service may be used or oper-

ated anywhere in the United States subject to the provisions of paragraph (d) of this section: *Provided,* That when the area of operation is changed for a period exceeding 7 days, the following procedure shall be observed:

(1) When the change of area of operation occurs inside the same Radio District, the Engineer in Charge of the Radio District involved and the Commission's office, Washington, D.C., 20554, shall be notified.

(2) When the station is moved from one Radio District to another, the Engineers in Charge of the two Radio Districts involved and the Commission's office, Washington, D.C., 20554, shall be notified.

(c) A Class C or Class D mobile station may be used or operated anywhere in the United States subject to the provisions of paragraph (d) of this section.

(d) A mobile station authorized in this service may be used or operated on any vessel, aircraft, or vehicle of the United States: *Provided,* That when such vessel, aircraft, or vehicle is outside the territorial limits of the United States, the station, its operation, and its operator shall be subject to the governing provisions of any treaty concerning telecommunications to which the United States is a party, and when within the territorial limits of any foreign country, the station shall be subject also to such laws and regulations of that country as may be applicable.

§95.119 Control points, dispatch points, and remote control.

(a) A control point is an operating position which is under the control and supervision of the licensee, at which a person immediately responsible for the proper operation of the transmitter is stationed, and at which adequate means are available to aurally monitor all transmissions and to render the transmitter inoperative. Each Class A base or fixed station shall be provided with a control point, the location of which will be specified in the license. The location of the control point must be the same as the transmitting equipment unless the application includes a request for a different location. Exception to the requirement for a control point may be made by the Commission upon specific request and justification therefor in the case of certain unattended Class A stations employing special emissions pursuant to §95.47 (e). Authority for such exception must be shown on the license.

(b) A dispatch point is any position from which messages may be transmitted under the supervision of the person at a control point who is responsible for the proper operation of the transmitter. No authorization is required to install dispatch points.

(c) Remote control of a Citizens radio station means the control of the transmitting equipment of that station from any place other than the location of the transmitting equipment, except that direct mechanical control or direct electrical control by wired connections of transmitting equipment from some other point on the same premises, craft, or vehicle shall not be considered remote control. A Class A base or fixed station may be authorized to be used or operated by remote control from another fixed location or from mobile units: *Provided*, That adequate means are available to enable the person using or operating the station to render the transmitting equipment inoperative from each remote control position should improper operation occur.

(d) Operation of any Class C or Class D station by remote control is prohibited except remote control by wire upon specific authorization by the Commission when satisfactory need is shown.

§95.121 Civil defense communications.

A licensee of a station authorized under this part may use the licensed radio facilities for the transmission of messages relating to civil defense activities in connection with official tests or drills conducted by, or actual emergencies proclaimed by, the civil defense agency having jurisdiction over the area in which the station is located: *Provided*, That:

(a) The operation of the radio station shall be on a voluntary basis.

(b) [Reserved]

(c) Such communications are conducted under the direction of civil defense authorities.

(d) As soon as possible after the beginning of such use, the licensee shall send notice to the Commission in Washington, D.C., and to the Engineer in Charge of the Radio District in which the station is located, stating the nature of the communications being transmitted and the duration of the special use of the station. In addition, the Engineer in Charge shall be notified as soon as possible of any change in the nature of or termination of such use.

(e) In the event such use is to be a series of pre-planned tests or drills of the same or similar nature which are scheduled in advance for specific times or at certain intervals of time, the licensee may send a single notice to the Commission in Washington, D.C., and to the Engineer in Charge of the Radio District in which the station is located, stating the nature of the communications to be transmitted, the duration of each such test, and the times scheduled for such use. Notice shall likewise be given in the event of any change in the nature of or termination of any such series of tests.

(f) The Commission may, at any time, order the discontinuance of such special use of the authorized facilities.

SUBPART E—

OPERATION OF CITIZENS RADIO STATIONS IN THE UNITED STATES BY CANADIANS

§95.131 Basis, purpose and scope.

(a) The rules in this subpart are based on, and are applicable solely to the agreement (TIAS #6931) between the United States and Canada, effective July 24, 1970, which permits Canadian stations in the General Radio Service to be operated in the United States.

(b) The purpose of this subpart is to implement the agreement (TIAS #6931) between the United States and Canada by prescribing rules under which a Canadian licensee in the General Radio Service may operate his station in the United States.

§95.133 Permit required.

Each Canadian licensee in the General Radio Service desiring to operate his radio station in the United States, under the provisions of the agreement (TIAS #6931), must obtain a permit for such operation from the Federal Communications Commission. A permit for such operation shall be issued only to a person holding a valid license in the General Radio Service issued by the appropriate Canadian governmental authority.

§95.135 Application for permit.

(a) Application for a permit shall be made on FCC Form 410–B. Form 410–B may be obtained from the Commission's Washington, D.C., office or from any of the Commission's field offices. A separate application form shall be filed for each station or transmitter desired to be operated in the United States.

(b) The application form shall be completed in full in English and signed by the applicant. The application must be filed by mail or in person with the Federal Communications Commission, Gettysburg, Pa. 17325, U.S.A. To allow sufficient time for processing, the application should be filed at least 60 days before the date on which the applicant desires to commence operation.

(c) The Commission, at its discretion, may require the Canadian licensee to give evidence of his knowledge of the Commission's applicable rules and regulations. Also the Commission may require the applicant to furnish any additional information it deems necessary.

§95.137 Issuance of permit.

(a) The Commission may issue a permit under such conditions, restrictions and terms as it deems appropriate.

(b) Normally, a permit will be issued to expire 1 year after issuance but in no event after the expiration of the license issued to the Canadian licensee by his government.

(c) If a change in any of the terms of a permit is desired, an application for modification of the permit is required. If operation beyond the expiration date of a permit is desired an application for renewal of the permit is required. Application for modification or for renewal of a permit shall be filed on FCC Form 410–B.

(d) The Commission, in its discretion, may deny any application for a permit under this subpart. If an application is denied, the applicant will be notified by letter. The applicant may, within 30 days of the mailing of such letter, request the Commission to reconsider its action.

§95.139 Modification or cancellation of permit.

At any time the Commission may, in its discretion, modify or cancel any permit issued under this subpart. In this event, the permittee will be notified of the Commission's action by letter mailed to his mailing address in the United States and the permittee shall comply immediately. A permittee may, within 30 days of the mailing of such letter, request the Commission to reconsider its action. The filing of a request for reconsideration shall not stay the effectiveness of that action, but the Commission may stay its action on its own motion.

§95.141 Possession of permit.

The current permit issued by the Commission, or a photocopy thereof, must be in the possession of the operator or attached to the transmitter. The license issued to the Canadian licensee by his government must also be in his possession while he is in the United States.

†95.143 Knowledge of rules required.

Each Canadian permittee, operating under this subpart, shall have read and understood this Part 95, Citizens Radio Service.

§95.145 Operating conditions.

(a) The Canadian licensee may not under any circumstances begin operation until he has received a permit issued by the Commission.

(b) Operation of station by a Canadian licensee under a permit issued by the Commission must comply with all of the following:

(1) The provisions of this subpart and of Subparts A through D of this part.

(2) Any further conditions specified on the permit issued by the Commission.

§95.147 Station identification.

The Canadian licensee authorized to operate his radio station in the United States under the provisions of this subpart shall identify his station by the call sign issued by the appropriate authority of the government of Canada followed by the station's geographical location in the United States as nearly as possible by city and state.

UNITED STATES OF AMERICA   FCC Form 452-C
FEDERAL COMMUNICATIONS COMMISSION   (July 1972)
TRANSMITTER IDENTIFICATION CARD

1. Station call sign:

2. Name and Address of Permittee or Licensee:

Transmitter Identification Card

This card must be affixed to the rear of a Citizens Radio set at a fixed or base location. For a mobile CB station, it must be kept as a part of permanent station records, but need not be affixed to the set.

The FCC Field Office Addresses

439 U.S. Courthouse& Customhouse
113 St. Joseph Street, Mobile AL 36602
205-433-3581, Ext. 209

U.S. Post Office Building,
Room G63, 4th and G Street, P.O. Box 644 Anchorage AK 99510
907-272-1822

U.S. Courthouse
Room 1754, 312 North Spring Street Los Angeles CA 90012
213-688-3276

Fox Theatre Building
1245 Seventh Avenue, San Diego CA 92101

300 South Ferry Street
Terminal Island, San Pedro CA 90731
213-831-9281

323A Customhouse
555 Battery Street, San Francisco CA 94111
415-556-7700

504 New Customhouse
19th St. between Cal. & Stout Sts. Denver CO 80202
303-837-4054

Room 216
1919 M Street, N.W., Washington DC 20554
202-632-7000

919 Federal Building
51 S.W. First Avenue, Miami FL 33130
305-350-5541

738 Federal Building
500 Zack Street, Tampa FL 33606
813-228-7711, Ext. 233

1602 Gas Light Tower
235 Peachtree Street, N.E., Atlanta GA 30303
404-526-6381

238 Federal Ofc. Bldg. & Courthouse
Bull and State Streets, P.O. Box 8004, Savannah GA 31402
912-232-4321, Ext. 320

502 Federal Building
P.O. Box 1021, Honolulu HI 96808
546-5640

37th Floor-Federal Bldg.
219 South Dearborn St., Chicago IL 60604
312-353-5386

829 Federal Building South
600 South Street, New Orleans LA 70130
504-527-2094

George M. Fallon Federal Bldg.
Room 819, 31 Hopkins Plaza, Baltimore MD 21201
301-962-2727

1600 Customhouse
India & State Streets, Boston MA 02109
617-223-6608

1054 Federal Building
Washington Blvd. & LaFayette Street, Detroit MI 48226
313-226-6077

691 Federal Building
4th & Robert Streets, St. Paul MN 55101
612-725-7819

1703 Federal Building
601 East 12th Street, Kansas City MO 64106
816-374-5526

905 Federal Building
111 W. Huron St. at Delaware Ave., Buffalo NY 14202
716-842-3216

748 Federal Building
641 Washington Street, New York NY 10014
212-620-5745

314 Multnomah Building
319 S.W. Pine Street, Portland OR 97204
503-221-3097

1005 U.S. Customhouse
2nd & Chestnut Streets, Philadelphia PA 19106
215-597-4410

U.S. Post Office & Customhouse
Room 322-323 P.O. Box 2987, San Juan PR 00903
809-722-4562

323 Federal Building
300 Willow Street, Beaumont TX 77701
713-838-0271, Ext. 317

Federal Building-U.S. Courthouse
Room 13E7, 1100 Commerce Street, Dallas TX 75202
214-749-3243

5636 Federal Building
515 Rusk Avenue, Houston TX 77002
713-226-4306

Military Circle
870 North Military Highway, Norfolk VA 23502
703-420-5100

8012 Federal Office Building
909 First Avenue, Seattle WA 96104
206-442-7653

Directory of Manufacturers

Listed below are manufacturers of Citizens Band radios and antennas and where they are located.

Radio manufacturers

Apelco
676 Island Pond Road
Manchester, NH 03103

Browning Laboratories, Inc.
1269 Union Ave.
Laconia, NH 03246

Courier
Fanon/Courier Corp.
990 S. Fair Oaks Ave.
Pasadena, CA 91005

Craig Corp.
921 W. Artesia Blvd.
Compton, CA 90220

Dynascan Corp.
1801 W. Belle Plaine Ave.
Chicago, IL 60613

E. F. Johnson Co.
Wauseca, MN 56093

Fieldmaster Radio Corp.
21212 Van Owen St.
Canoga Park, CA 91303

Handic of U.S.A.
14340 N.W. 60th St.
Miami Lakes, FL 33104

Hy-Gain Electronics Corp.
R.R. #3
Lincoln, NB 68505

J.I.L. Corp. of America
1000 E. Del Amo Blvd.
Carson, CA 90746

Lafayette Radio Electronics
Corp.
111 Jericho Turnpike
Syosset, NY, 11791

Midland International Corp.
P.O. Box 19032
Kansas City, MO 64141

Olson Electronics
260 S. Forge St.
Akron, OH 44327

Pace Communications
24049 S. Frampton Ave.
Harbor City, CA 90710

PAL Electronics
2962 W. Weldon
Phoenix, AZ 85017

Panasonic
One Panasonic Way
Secaucus, NJ 07094

Pearce-Simpson
P.O. Box 520800, Biscayne
Annex
Miami, FL 33152

Radio Shack
2617 W. 7th St.
Fort Worth, TX 76107

Ray Jefferson
Main and Cotton Streets
Philadelphia, PA 19127

Regency Electronics, Inc.
7707 Records St.
Indianapolis, IN 46226

Robyn International, Inc.
P.O. Box 478
Rockford, MI 49341

Royce Electronics Corp.
1142 Clay St.
North Kansas City, MO 64116

SBE Linear Systems, Inc.
220 Airport Blvd.
Watsonville, CA 95076

Sharp Electronics Corp.
10 Keystone Place
Paramus, NJ 07652

Sonar Radio Corp.
73 Wortman Ave.
Brooklyn, NY 11207

Sony Corp. of America
714 Fifth Ave.
New York, NY 10019

Standard Communications
108 W. Victoria St.
Carson, CA 90248

Teaberry Electronics Corp.
4655 Massachusetts Ave.
Indianapolis, IN 46218

Tram/Diamond Corp.
Lower Bay Road
Winnisquam, NH 03289

XTAL
9749 Shirley Ave.
Northridge, CA 91324

Antenna Manufacturers

Antenna, Inc.
23850 Commerce Park Road
Cleveland, OH 44122

Avanti Research & Development, Inc.
340 Stewart Ave.
Addison, IL 60101

Blue Streak
200 E. Wilshire Ave.
Santa Ana, CA 92705

Breaker Corp.
110 Great Southwest Parkway
Arlington, TX 76011

Cushcraft Corp.
621 Hayward St.
Manchester NH 03103

GC Electronics
400 S. Wyman St.
Rockford, IL 61101

Gotham
2051 N.W. Second Ave.
Miami, FL 33127

Hustler
New-Tronics Corp.
15800 Commerce Park Drive
Brook Park, OH 44142

Hy-Gain Electronics Corp.
R.R. #3
Lincoln, NB 68505

Lafayette Radio Electronics
Corp.
111 Jericho Turnpike
Syosset, NY 11791

Radio Shack
2617 W. 7th St.
Fort Worth, TX 76107

Robyn International, Inc.
P.O. Box 478
Rockford, MI 49341

Shakespeare Industrial
Fiberglass Div.
P.O. Drawer 246
Columbia, SC 29202

Turner Co., Inc.
909 17th St. N.E.
Cedar Rapids, IA 52402

Form Approved
GAO No B-180227(R01 02)

United States of America
Federal Communications Commission

APPLICATION FOR CLASS C OR D STATION
LICENSE IN THE CITIZENS RADIO SERVICE

FCC FORM 505

December 1974

Instructions

A Use a typewriter or print clearly in capital letters. Stay within the boxes. Skip a box where a space would normally appear.

B Sign and date application.

C Enclose appropriate fee with application. DO NOT SUBMIT CASH. Make check or money order payable to Federal Communications Commission. No fee is required for an application filed by a governmental entity. For additional fee details, including amount and exemptions, see Subpart G of Part I, FCC Rules and Regulations.

D Do not enclose order form or subscription fee for FCC Rules.

E MAIL APPLICATION TO FEDERAL COMMUNICATIONS COMMISSION, GETTYSBURG, PA. 17325.

NOTE:
Do not operate until you have your own license Use of any call sign not your own is prohibited

1. Complete if license is for an individual

Applicant's First Name   Init.   Last

2 Date of Birth

Month   Day   Year

3. Complete if license is for a business

Applicant's Name of Business, Organization, Or Partnership

4. Mailing Address (Number and Street) If P.O. Box or RFD# Is Used Also Fill Out Items 8 – 10.

5. City

6. State

7. Zip Code

9. City

10. State

11. Type of Applicant (Check one)

☐ Individual ☐ Association ☐ Corporation

☐ Business Partnership ☐ Governmental - Entity

☐ Sole Proprietor or Individual/Doing Business As

☐ Other (Specify)

13. This application is for (Check only one)

☐ Class C Station License
(NON-VOICE—REMOTE CONTROL OF MODELS)

☐ Class D Station License (VOICE)

15. Certification I certify that:

• The applicant is not a foreign government or a representative thereof.

• The applicant has (or has ordered from the Government Printing Office) a current copy of Part 95 of the Commission's rules governing the Citizens Radio Service.

• The applicant will operate his transmitter in full compliance with the applicable law and current rules of the FCC and that his station will not be used for any purpose contrary to Federal, State, or local law or with greater power than authorized

• The applicant waives any claim against the regulatory power of the United States relative to the use of a particular frequency or the use of the medium of transmission of radio waves because of any such previous use, whether licensed or unlicensed.

12. This application is for

☐ New License

☐ Renewal

☐ Increase in Number of Transmitters

IMPORTANT
Give Current Call Sign

14. Indicate number of transmitters applicant will operate during the five year license period (Check one)

☐ 1 to 5 ☐ 6 to 15 ☐ 16 or more (Specify No. and attach statement justifying need.)

WILLFUL FALSE STATEMENTS MADE ON THIS FORM OR AT-TACHMENTS ARE PUNISHABLE BY FINE AND IMPRISONMENT. U.S. CODE, TITLE 18, SECTION 1001.

16. _____

Signature of Individual applicant, or authorized person on behalf of a governmental entity or partnership, or an officer of a corporation or association

17. Date _____

Notes

You'll be keeping this invaluable book near your CB set for reference. While you're driving, you'll be almost certain to hear CB expressions that are not included here. (CB is such a varied and fast-changing language that no single book could possibly hope to keep up with all the words and phrases.) As soon as you stop, we suggest that you write down these new terms here before you forget them. If you care to send them along to the publishers, we can assure you that we'll be very grateful.

Name _____

Address _____

City _____

Zip, state _____

"Handle" _____ Call sign _____

DATE TIME	STATION	FREQ.	END OF QSO	LOCATION & MISC. INFO.

DATE TIME	STATION	FREQ.	END OF QSO	LOCATION & MISC. INFO.

DATE TIME	STATION	FREQ.	END OF QSO	LOCATION & MISC. INFO.

DATE TIME	STATION	FREQ.	END OF QSO	LOCATION & MISC. INFO.

DATE TIME	STATION	FREQ.	END OF QSO	LOCATION & MISC. INFO.

DATE TIME	STATION	FREQ.	END OF QSO	LOCATION & MISC. INFO.

DATE TIME	STATION	FREQ.	END OF QSO	LOCATION & MISC. INFO.

DATE TIME	STATION	FREQ.	END OF QSO	LOCATION & MISC. INFO.